MW00777254

OLD FARTS ON A BUS

BY C. A. HOCKING

Copyright © C. A. HOCKING 2018
ISBN: 9780975849026

All rights reserved. Without limiting the rights under copyright above, no part of this publication shall be reproduced, stored in or introduced into a retrieval system, or transmitted in any form or by any means (electronic, mechanical, photocopying, recording or otherwise), without the prior permission of the copyright owner of this book. Enquiries should be addressed to the author at:
www.cahocking.com

DEDICATION

To all of us Old Farts for whom
getting old is not a burden, but a privilege
we lived long enough to enjoy.

Also by C. A. HOCKING

A PLACE IN TIME
DAMAGED GOODS
HOME TO ROOST
THE SARAH ANN ELLIOTT SERIES
THE AUNT EDNA STORIES

DISCLAIMER

All characters and events appearing in this
work are fictitious. Any resemblance to real
persons, living or dead, is purely a result of your
paranoia. Get over it. And enjoy the ride!

PROLOGUE

THE PREPARATION

There are many reasons why people travel. When you are young and unencumbered, it is simply what you do when you are young and unencumbered. You throw a few things into a backpack, book some cheap flights, load the devices with GPS and relevant information and off you go. You stay in cheap hostels, travel on buses, trains, horses, donkeys, camels, bicycles and on foot, eat whatever is on the go, drink the local booze, have safe sex with whomever you fancy and go back home to your parents' house to turn it into a tip until you've saved enough money for the next trip.

However, things aren't quite so easy for us Old Farts. Did I hear you say, "Please explain what an Old Fart is?" Well, to keep things simple, let's say it is anyone over the age of 60. There are younger people with the mentality of an Old Fart, but once you hit 60, you are the real deal, whether you like it or not. You've raised the children or not, depending on your lifestyle choices; are probably a grandparent; have either retired or are contemplating retirement; are set in ways that makes concrete look like water; either have hang-ups about your weight/saggy bits/stretch marks/turkey neck/grey hair/erectile dysfunction/lack of libido, or are at complete peace with all of the former; have developed a great sense of humour about your fellow human beings and their foibles or sit in judgement about them and find them lacking; and have a sense of time running out in which to do the things you always wanted to do. And travel is often one of those things.

2009 had been a difficult year, with the usual Old Fart illnesses, dramas with various children, and house renovations which seemed to go on forever. Another cold Canberra winter was approaching in 2010 and we were ready for a holiday. It was Hubby who saw the luxury package tour combination advertised by a company we had travelled with before and found to be very amenable. The first eleven days would be in Egypt (this was before the Arab Spring, when Egypt was still the go-to destination for Aussies), then two and a half weeks in Italy, ending with a third month-long tour of the great gardens of France, Belgium, The Netherlands, Austria, Germany and Switzerland. By then, we'll have had enough of being on a bus and plan to hire a car and visit Hubby's relatives in England and Scotland for a couple of weeks.

We paid our deposit and had a month to prepare. Which is quite a big deal for us. You see, Old Farts can't just throw a few things in a backpack and take off. For a start, our medication alone will usually fill a backpack. Most of us travel with a bag of pills and potions and a letter from our doctor stating what they are, in case we are stopped at an airport by Customs when the sniffer dogs mistake our arthritis painkillers for heroin. Most of us are on cholesterol lowering drugs and aspirin to thin the blood, that's just a given these days. Then there are the gut medications to keep us regular (they can take up a lot of space), the various painkillers for the various types of pain that go with growing older, the hormone replacement therapy and lubricant for women, the Viagra for men, the medications for heart disease, kidney disease, cancer, diabetes, irritable bowel syndrome, anti-histamines, vitamins, calcium, anti-depressants, stimulants, uppers, downers - and the list goes on and on and on. My medication bag alone weighed in at a kilogram. Hubby's was somewhat lighter.

Then there are the other essentials. Sunscreen. Insect repellent. Anti-itch cream for the insect bites that got through the repellent. And soothing cream for when the sunscreen doesn't work. Antiseptic cream. And of course, the antiseptic hand wipes and hand lotion. A must for those parts of the world that aren't ... well ... clean.

Then we come to the clothing. Old Farts feel the cold, so we take layers. In fact, I like to think of us as Sarah Lee travellers - layer upon layer upon layer. We also feel the heat and humidity, what with menopausal hot flushes and medication side effects, so we need to have cotton and linen in the mix as well. A young female traveller once told me that you only need to take three pairs of underpants, a packet of small panty liners, a small box of tampons, a spare pair of jeans, two extra t-shirts and good walking shoes. You wear a fresh panty liner each day and only change your knickers every three or four days. And then those itty-bitty undies rinse out in the sink and dry off with a hair dryer.

Bless her dear naive youthful good intentions.

A young body discharges so neatly, and young knickers need a magnifying glass to find them, they are so small. Old bodies of both genders discharge at an alarming rate from all orifices, and granny knickers need a blow torch to dry them, they are so big. And while panty liners are OK for young females, many post-menopausal women need a little more, so incontinence pads of various bladder leakage ratings go into the suitcase and, damn it, they take up a lot of room. But you gotta have them because you can't just go and change your knickers every time you sneeze or cough in the middle of Abu Simbel or the Vatican City.

Male Old Farts often need a little something as well, usually a longer version of the panty liner, because you can never trust a fart as they tend to leave streak marks, which can be rather difficult to wash out in the sink. Those little bars of soap that hotel rooms provide can dissolve quite quickly in the desperate attempts to remove said brown marks.

Now, for the clothes. Our tour was going to Egypt, Europe and Britain. Just over two months in May, June and July and several different climates. Starting with Egypt, you need sandals, leather of course, so your feet don't sweat against cheap plastic. Not thongs, because they can slip and falling is a big concern for Old Farts. And they have to have good orthopaedic soles if you are going to handle all the walking, so it's Old Fart sandals for everyone. Then it's shorts for the men, regardless of age, because men can get away with shorts. But not women.

There are some things that women over 60 should definitely not do - wear sleeveless tops (wrinkled armpits arrgh!), low necklines (corrugated cleavage arrgh!), and shorts (cellulite and saggy knees arrgh!). On the other hand, the fashion for three-quarter pants and orthopaedic sandals isn't much better. Let's face it - after 60, most of us have not only lost our waistlines, we've lost all trace of recognisable feminine shape to become amorphic, frumpy, dumpy and asexual in appearance. There are the occasional slim, shapely exceptions and don't we hate them! So the uniform for most Old Fart females in hot weather seems to be a big boxy shapeless cotton/linen shirt (t-shirts cling to the lumpy bits too much), cotton three-quarter pants with the hemline flapping around at the calf to expose those thick spider-veined ankles, and the orthopaedic sandals that make your feet look fat and clumpy, no matter how carefully you have done that home pedicure, which incidentally put your back out in the process of trying to reach those toenails to paint them bright red as an expression of your free-spirited personality. Which no-one will believe you have anyway.

And don't forget the hat! It has to be a travel hat which will squash flat in the suitcase, so no chance of a nice straw hat with a turned up brim. No, it's the lawn bowler's cloth hat with the floppy brim, and if you've really thought it through, will tie under the chin so that it doesn't blow off in the wind. And the hat negates the need for too much hair product in the suitcase, as hat hair is hat hair, not matter how much you fuss with it in the morning. Hat on, fine. Hat off, hat hair. Flat hat hair. Which isn't even noticeable for most female Old Farts as they've long ago succumbed to the Short Back And Sides Suburban Blob Hairdo anyway. Besides which, we all know that no one is looking at us. Female Old Farts are basically invisible to anyone under 50. On the other hand, between the ages of 50 and 59, females spend a lot of time looking at us over-60's with dread and fear, and a fierce determination not to end up looking like us. Well, I've got news for them!

So, where were we? I digress. I'm an Old Fart, it's what we do.

That's right, we have the summer clothes in place. Now for the colder weather clothes. We are going to the top of a mountain in Europe on our tour, Mount Jungfrau to be precise, where we are told the temperature could be −20C. So it's thermals, long sleeved tops, jackets and parkas, woolly hats, scarves and gloves as well as our good, closed orthopaedic walking shoes and thermal socks. They forgot to tell us that the tourist centre at the top of the mountain is heated and, after we've ventured outside for thirty seconds to experience the freezing, thin mountain air above the amazing glaciers, we go back inside, light headed and nauseated with altitude sickness, and fry! We sit around tables eating sausage rolls and drinking bad coffee with the sweat pouring off us, swearing that next time we come, we'll know better. All the while knowing that there won't be a next time.

Now, for the last thing to go into the suitcase. The pseudo-essentials. For us female Old Farts, it's the cosmetics bag. Make-up (after all, there will be other women on the tour and one must maintain one's standards); hair products, small straightening/curling iron despite the former comments about Hat Hair (hotel rooms only have hairdryers which doesn't give your hair the polished look); costume jewellery that we won't miss if it gets stolen (there will be several dress-up dinners, so we have to take day jewellery, night jewellery and show-off jewellery); manicure and pedicure essentials (I know we aren't supposed to take flammables onto aircraft, but surely a little bottle of nail polish and remover doesn't count?); and bathroom essentials - skincare, deodorant, moisturising soap (only men use those little soaps provided by the hotels), a lady razor (no stubbly legs puleese!) and the best shampoo and conditioner. Enough for two months. That adds up to quite a bit. We can hopefully buy other bits and pieces over there, like hair spray (because hat hair needs a bit of zooshing up before going to dinner in the evenings) and lubricant (which we all forgot to pack because quite frankly, sex wasn't high on our list of priorities at the time) and so on and so forth.

The male Old Farts, on the other hand, pack a razor and shaving brush. They use the soap and shampoo provided by the hotels. What they spend time packing is their version of the essentials. They start with the iPhone (or version thereof); the Mac laptop (or version thereof); the iPad (or...well, you get the drift); the eReader; the video camera; the normal camera; the iPod; and all the chargers and cords and attachments that go with each device. They have arranged for global roaming on their phones, GPS for each country they are visiting to be downloaded on their tablets and phones, the latest data packages, and hours and hours of music downloaded onto their iPods which they will never actually listen to, but it gave them an excuse not to get involved with their wives' endless discussions about which jewellery goes with which outfit and does my bum look big in this baggy pair of three quarter pants?

And they pack their Blueys. That's Old Fart Speak for Viagra. Because, unlike female Old Farts, males do have sex on their minds. For them, a holiday means more sex, but they soon find out that the pace of the guided tour is, as one male Old Fart so aptly put it, "the best form of birth control ever invented!" So they usually get home with almost as many Blueys as they left with. But hope springs eternal and there's no harm in packing a few tablets.

So. We are almost ready to leave. I'm satisfied that I haven't left anything out and Hubby is satisfied that he hasn't forgotten any chargers for his gadgets. We've notified the family and friends, arranged for someone to take care of the pets and plants, got our anti-theft bags and wallets in place, weighed our suitcases and repacked at least six times until we get the weight right, sorted our credit cards and currency conversion for each country, tried to lose a couple of kilos because we know we'll eat a lot and put on weight, then gave up and resolved to go on a diet when we get home - and we're off to the airport.

The airport. Oh dear. That's the part of travel I find the hardest. I suffer from flight nerves, which takes the form of rapid heart beat, sweating and diarrhoea, and need to take Valium to fly. I have discovered I am one of many with this complaint. We either take Valium or Beta-blockers. I find the Valium very effective. But my flight nerves start the minute I wake up on the day we leave and go straight to the bowel. Very inconvenient. So it's a Valium on waking, which makes it hard to wake up. But I keep moving through the Valium induced haze. We're very organised between my several visits to the loo, get to the airport with time to spare, check in, then go for a coffee after I visit the loo again. When it's time to go through security, it's a quick visit to the loo - again. Then we are lining up with hundreds of other people waiting to go through Customs. I get that urgent need again and look around for a loo. We are trapped between security and Customs and there are no loos to be seen. I ask a security officer if there is a loo nearby. I am sweating and anxious and rather desperate. She looks at me suspiciously. Am I concealing drugs within my person and needing a loo to dispose of them? She gives me a steely look and tells me there is no toilet nearby. Hubby looks concerned and says, "Clench!" I clench! The queue moves slowly, oh so bloody slowly, and finally we are through. I streak to the loo. The relief brings tears to my eyes. I take another Valium.

The rest of the boarding procedure is a blur. Once settled on the plane, I should have slipped into a peaceful snooze, but I am one of those unfortunates who simply cannot sleep sitting up - and we are travelling cattle class. We are breaking up the 23 hour trip with a stopover in Singapore, and for 8 hours, I sit upright in a haze of Valium, feeling cranky and cheated because everyone on the plane seems to be asleep except for me. However, if you ask around, many people have trouble sleeping sitting up. In fact, after this trip, we have decided that we will only travel overseas again if we can afford Business Class and lie down. I'd better sell a few more books if we want to do that!

Our overnight stay at the Airport Hotel at Singapore is wonderful. So good, in fact, that Hubby gets online and changes our return flight to allow for a four day stopover in Singapore on the way home. We book into a good hotel opposite the old Raffles Hotel for those four days and realise we will be there to celebrate our wedding anniversary. Lovely!

Then we get on the plane for the 15 hour flight to Cairo. A pointless sleeping tablet, three movies, three meals and four snacks later and we arrive at the Cairo airport.

And begin our tour.

DAY 1

EGYPT: THE MEET AND GREET

Our connection with the tour is to meet us at the Cairo Airport. After we navigate our way through Customs and security and try to ignore the fact that every security officer and policeman is carrying a semi-automatic rifle (not something we see in Australia), we retrieve our suitcases and look for our transport to the hotel. The tour has guaranteed that we will be picked up and it will all be hassle free. It would be, if we could only find our name amongst the hundreds of names written in various shades of faded felt pen on bits of tatty cardboard being waved about by bored looking Egyptians for whom this task must be ... well ... boring! It takes us half an hour to find our bit of cardboard with the tour company logo in tiny letters, Hubby's surname

13

misspelled and mine in small letters in brackets underneath. Like an after thought. I guess the Egyptians aren't too familiar with wives keeping their maiden names after marriage and were possibly confused by the fact that we are travelling as husband and wife, but have different surnames. Or they thought we were lovers on a holiday, which makes us more interesting than we actually are.

Anyway, the driver loads our luggage into the back of a battered mini-bus, we board with several other flight-weary travellers, none of whom are on our tour or going to our hotel, and enter...gasp... Cairo traffic!

We thought we had become accustomed to different driving conditions in different countries, some of them quite frightening, but Cairo traffic is a riot! Our flight had arrived at sunrise and by the time we hit the road, we are in the midst of morning peak hour. If there are road rules in Cairo, no one obeys them. A three-lane highway has up to eight cars fighting for space across it, door to door sideways and bumper to bumper in front and behind, and they don't drive with their motors, they drive with their car horns. The sound is deafening! I see that our driver is unconcerned, in complete control and at perfect ease with his surroundings, so I relax and enjoy the scramble going on around us. We observe that every car is dented to some degree and are only shocked by the first few minor accidents we see. After that, it becomes a form of entertainment. We watch as the cars that connect with a crunch stop, the drivers get out, examine their damage, shrug their shoulders and get back into their vehicles to continue their journey. No one around them appears to take any notice, except to honk their horns even harder until the stationary vehicles are moving again.

The traffic is moving quite slowly and one of the other passengers asks the driver if it is always like this. He says, "No, today is a good day. Very easy today." The passenger then asks him if there are always so many accidents. The driver shrugs his shoulders and says, "Many accidents, but not many deaths. Too slow for deaths. Only deaths out on the desert roads where they go fast."

OK.

We are reassured.

Our hotel is first on the drop-off schedule. It is very grand, formerly a king's palace with the original magnificent building preserved, and new accommodation and beautiful gardens tastefully added around it. And a four metre high security fence with armed policemen (again with the semi-automatic rifles) stationed at each boundary. Our mini-bus is stopped at the gate and sniffer dogs and men with mirrors check around and under the bus. One of the passengers asks if this is normal and our driver says, "Yes. This is normal since the Luxor Massacre in 1997."

The passenger has to ask, "The Luxor Massacre? I've never heard of that."

The driver gives him a pitying look and says, "Some terrorists killed 62 tourists at Hatshepsut's Tomb. Very bad for business. So now we are more careful."

Oh.

Again, we are reassured. I think. Although the tourist who asked the question has gone white as a sheet.

There is more security as we pass through the hotel entrance, including another security gate. Hubby has a pacemaker and can't go through them. He must discard his backpack, watch, pocket contents, belt and shoes each time. This is the fourth time since we got off the plane. He's looking a bit miffed. But when we are shown to our room, our spirits lift. We have a large, modern room with a big balcony overlooking the Nile River. We can see Cairo, alive and bustling amongst the modern and ancient buildings. There is no other place like Egypt in the world, with 82 million people clinging to the banks of a single river, nearly 7 million of them living in this unique city. And there is a real energy rising out of the bustle, something positive, almost exciting it is so tangible. Despite all the semi-automatic machine guns and uniformed police on every corner, we feel safe and welcomed.

We close the doors, turn the air conditioning up and fall into bed for a few hours.

We rise later, freshen up and dress in cotton and linen casuals for the Meet and Greet that always precedes these tours. We had been told by our travel agent back home that our tour would comprise of middle class Australians, Canadians and Americans. Middle class - they'd have to be to afford this trip. A good mix of backgrounds. We have travelled with this combination before and enjoyed it very much. We look forward to meeting them all.

Our tour guide meets us at the reception room door where our tour company logo is displayed in much larger letters than at the airport. She is a delight. Mid thirties, pretty, curvaceous, English with a very posh accent and the biggest, warmest smile you can imagine. Her name is Leslie. She pins our name tags onto us and ushers us into the room with a jolly, "Just introduce yourselves around and mingle. I'll be with you when everyone is here." We love her on sight. Always a good start.

It's a cocktail party with dinner to follow. We take a couple of drinks, orange juice for me and champagne for Hubby, and approach the nearest couple. Fellow Australians. A neatly dressed 60-something woman with teased-and-smoothed shoulder length blonde hair and too much make up, including false eyelashes, not a good look at our age. She is wearing a beige and black top and black trousers with beige ballet flats. Almost tasteful, except for the fat arms bulging from the too short sleeves of the polyester top and the tummy-enhancing elastic waist of the black polyester trousers, which are a fraction too short above the shoes. She is posturing, holding her champagne glass a little too high and looking around her with a superior air. She believes she is the most elegant woman in the room. But I've got news for her. You can't look elegant in polyester. Not ever. It's a myth perpetrated by chain store fashion houses who have their clothes made cheaply in China, then slap a label on them and sell them for 1000% profit margin. No, even if the beige is called cappuccino this season, polyester is simply not elegant.

Her makeup is thick, but reasonably stable in the air conditioned room and her bright red lipstick perfectly matches the long, pointed claw-like finger nails. I haven't seen nails like that for years. Very Dolly Parton. She seems to be talking too loudly, trying too hard, the smile too forced as if it's hard work. She flaps her hands around a lot when she talks to show off her nails. They look like they could sever a carotid artery if you got too close. It's hard to judge her age under all that thick makeup, until she turns her head sideways and the turkey neck tells me she's closer to 70 than 60.

Her husband is short, pot bellied, grey haired and has definitely seen his 70th birthday. He is rather loud and looking around him with an equally superior air.

Hubby and I introduce ourselves. And then that thing happens that only happens between Old Farts. When young people meet for the first time, they all ask each other what they do, male and female alike. Younger men and women all have jobs/careers, even if the women are taking time out to be at home with their young children. They usually had a job/career before the babies started coming and many of them plan to resume that job/career when the children are older. So they ask males and females, "What do you do?"

Not so with Old Farts. We introduce ourselves to our fellow travellers and he says to Hubby, "And what do you do?"

Hubby replies, "I'm a retired IT consultant. What about you?"

"Real estate."

To which his wife quickly adds, "But retired now."

He ignores me. That always pisses me off. So I direct my question to her. "And what do you do?"

To which he quickly replies disparagingly, "She does nothing. Nothing at all."

I say, "No one does nothing at all."

He glares at me. I wasn't supposed to stick up for her. He says, "She's just a housewife."

She is looking very sullen, which makes me think she's been subjected to this sort of put-down before. I say, in her defence, "So you raised the children, ran the home, did all the shopping, cooking, cleaning, ironing, gardening, banking, nursed your children and husband when they were sick, made sure your husband came home every day to a clean house and a good meal - and got no time off and no appreciation. I think what you did is the most important thing any woman ever does in her life. Well done!"

She looks at me gratefully and opens her mouth to say something, but he cuts in with, "We have a Social Set."

A what? I sense a bit of fun coming on. I feign serious interest and let him continue.

"We meet once a month at each other's houses. We know good food and good wine. Yes, we have a Social Set." Yessiree, he really did say that. He looks smug, as if he's somehow put me in my place. Well,

I know my place and it isn't where he thinks he put me!

I dub him and his wife Mr and Mrs Socially Superior. I can never remember names. But I never forget personalities.

I am delighted by this conversation. I have a perverse side to my nature that, when confronted with eccentric or badly behaved people, makes me want to draw them out to see just how far they will go. Hubby is sometimes amused by this and sometimes rather scared. This time, he is amused. I say, "That sounds wonderful. And where do you live?"

He names a small country town in Tasmania and asks me where we live. "Canberra."

"Canberra! With all those politicians!"

Hubby loves to correct people on this point. "No, the politicians don't live in Canberra. They live where you live. They only come to Canberra when Parliament is sitting. We have less politicians in Canberra than you have."

"But you've got the Prime Minister."

"And a big high wall around The Lodge so we never have to see her."

Mrs Socially Superior finally speaks. The mention of the Prime Minister has brought her to life again. She waves her red claws around and states, "And wouldn't it be a good thing if The Lodge burned down and her with it!"

OK. Bad move. They have stated their political leanings. There are two subjects that must be avoided on a tour like this - religion and politics. Time to redirect the conversation. Hubby says, "My wife is a writer."

Suddenly, I am subjected to a look of pure hatred from Mrs Socially Superior. It nearly knocks me over. She wanted me to be a housewife, too. After all, I'm plain and rather ordinary looking. I have no right not to be a housewife. I have let her down.

Mr Socially Superior gives me a belittling look, imagining me scribbling away with a pencil on a piece of paper in some suburban writer's group with a bunch of other plain, ordinary looking suburban women. He looks away and addresses Hubby as if I'm not there. "Anything published?"

Hubby says, "Yes, two very successful novels, one of which was shortlisted for a literary award, and a TV series which is in pre-production."

He looks taken aback. He is out of his depth for a moment. But only for a moment. I mean, after all, he has a Social Set. He knows how to make good conversation to go with the good food and good wine. He looks condescendingly at my glass of orange juice, takes a half step away from me to stand a little closer to Hubby and addresses him. "Do you drink good wine?"

I have been dismissed. I am loving this!

Hubby says politely, "Whatever comes out of my cellar. I'm not too fussy."

He lifts his nose in the air and says, "Well, we are!"

"Yes," she concurs vehemently, "we are!" The red nails are cutting a swathe through the air. I take a step back to protect myself.

They have finally found a way to place us socially and are looking down their noses at us, well satisfied. I am on the brink of bursting into laughter. No one can be Socially Superior in elastic waisted trousers with fat arms bulging out of a polyester top, outdated manicure, pot bellied husband and from a small town in Tasmania. But I won't tell them that.

I hope my delighted grin is interpreted as a socially polite smile.

My glass is almost empty, Hubby sees that dangerous, gleeful look in my eye and says, "We'd better go top up our glasses. Nice meeting you." He leads me away and we leave Mr and Mrs Socially Superior on their quest for someone better suited to their social standing. Poor darlings. They didn't find anyone who came up to their imaginary standards during the whole tour.

The next couple we talk to are also Australian, very chatty, very confident and very, very full of themselves. In the first ten seconds, we learn that he is a retired scientist who formerly worked in a research department of a university. And he also knows good food and good wine, which we believe because he's wearing all of it around his voluminous waistline.

She is a doctor, but not the medical kind, the kind with a PhD in something incredibly important, like the sex life of pond slime, and lectured at the same university that her husband worked at until their retirement. I can picture her lecturing a group of uni students. She has that air of authority about her, and you would cross her at your own peril. She sports the classic grey Short Back And Sides Suburban Blob haircut, sensible clothes and shoes, and no make-up. A true academic.

They tell us that they collect rare books and are much travelled. Mr and Mrs Intelligentsia. I am tempted to direct them to Mr and Mrs Socially Superior and then stand by and watch them compete. But that would be impolite. I might be perverse and a bit naughty, but I am not impolite.

Mr Intelligentsia asks Hubby what he does. "I'm a retired IT consultant and my wife is a writer." Mr Intelligentsia's eyes light up. Could he have found a fellow Intelligentsia in me?

"Published?" He directs the question towards me.

"Yes. Two books and a TV series in pre-production."

"What sort of books?"

"Novels."

Whoops. That answer wasn't up to standard. He is looking doubtful.

"What sort of novels?"

"Dark dramatic fiction."

"You don't write for the Young Adult market, do you?" he asks fearfully, as if he might catch something off me.

"No. My books are very adult. One is about domestic violence, the other about child abuse."

Mrs Intelligentsia becomes interested. "Where did you do your research?"

"I listened to many, many victims of domestic violence and child abuse and told their stories."

"But who did you consult professionally?"

"No one. My books give a voice to the victims, not the professions associated with them."

She gives me a scathing look. I'm clearly not very bright. "So what is your TV series about?"

"It's a narrative comedy."

"Oh." She doesn't know what to make of that. I have confused her. "And you live in Canberra?" She makes it sound like a last resort.

"Yes. What about you?"

"Sydney."

"Sydney? I lived in Sydney before moving to Canberra. Whereabouts?"

"Neutral Bay." She looks smug. It's a good suburb on the North Shore. "We have a lovely view of the Harbour."

"Oh, I know Neutral Bay well. I used to visit a friend there. In fact, I could see her place from mine."

"Really? Where were you living?"

"Right across the Harbour from you. At Double Bay."

"And you had Harbour views?"

"Yes. And isn't the Harbour lovely? One of the truly beautiful parts of the world."

Two deep frown lines appear between Mrs Intelligentsia's heavy, unplucked eyebrows. Double Bay ups Neutral Bay by at least one rung on the socio-economic ladder. I omit to tell her that I was divorced at the time, working in a job I hated because my writing wasn't making enough money to live on back then, alone after the last of my children had grown and flown, in a crappy little flat that I was paying too much for and which smelled of the previous tenant's cats, and had not yet met Hubby who eventually whisked me away to a better life in Canberra. And that my friend in Neutral Bay was in similar straits in a tired old block of flats with a lift that kept breaking down and trapping her inside it. And that my view was from the corner of my kitchen window where I could see an inch wide glimpse of the Harbour between the neighbouring red-brick blocks of flats, and that my friend's block of flats just happened to be within that narrow view.

Hubby is on to me and says, "We'd better top up our drinks," and we smile and move on. He is giving me that, "Please behave yourself," look. It hasn't been a promising start. But the next couple put everything to rights again.

They are in their 60's, tanned and healthy looking and instantly recognisable as from the Far North of Australia by their bright, light cotton clothes and complete lack of affectation. They are from Darwin, she a retired teacher and he a retired builder. She is nearly jumping out of her skin with excitement, whereas he is very still and quiet.

"Isn't it thrilling to be here? In Egypt! With all those pyramids and temples! And the Nile right there outside our hotel room!"

I feel the same way. "Yes, it's fabulous. I've wanted to visit Egypt my whole life."

"Me too! I've read so many books on Ancient Egypt! I can't believe we'll finally see it all!" She's bouncing around so much that she spills her champagne. "Oops, mustn't waste the cham-pag-nee!" she jokes and laughs loudly. I'm in love with Mrs Effusive. Her enthusiasm is catching. She turns to Mr Effusive who hasn't said much at all and hands him the glass. "Refill?" He silently takes the glass and goes to get the refill. She continues to chatter and laugh. He returns with the glass and, as he hands it to her, says quietly, "You haven't worn them out yet, have you?"

Mrs Effusive giggles. "Not yet, but there's still time." He smiles and resumes his silent stillness. They seem to be a perfect foil for each other. He's as laconic as she is exuberant and they are in complete accord.

One of the things that Hubby and I have observed about Old Fart couples who travel on these tours is that they generally get along very well together, in their own particular way. It's a plus when you have to spend an extended amount of time in a confined area in sometimes demanding circumstances with so many people. We haven't yet come across a couple who didn't get along in their own unique way, although after meeting Mr and Mrs Socially Superior, I wonder briefly if they might break the pattern. But it's too early to make a call on that. Mostly, couples get along. Perhaps couples who don't get along don't travel together. Probably a wise thing. And we have travelled with wives who have left their husbands at home for either health reasons or because the husband simply didn't like to travel. But we've never struck a husband who has travelled without a wife. Never quite worked out why.

So we chat with Mr and Mrs Effusive for a while, or at least with Mrs Effusive with an occasional grunt from her husband, then move on to the next couple.

They are Canadian. He is a retired accountant and she a retired paralegal. She has a warmth and natural ease and is the conversationalist of the two, while he seems the quieter one. At first, we are a bit taken aback at his quietness and the way he looks down when we are talking, as if he isn't paying attention, but then he looks up with a sudden cheeky grin, his mouth turned up at the corners just a little, a twinkle in his eye, and says something surprising, something funny, something clever and we all laugh. And I see that same twinkle in his wife's eyes every time she sees it in his. She knows something amusing is coming and she enjoys it.

Mrs Twinkling Eyes is quite tall and has the bearing of one who was once quite a beauty and aware of it. Not arrogance, just self-confidence. She is a little thicker around the waist these days, but superbly put together - hair, makeup, clothes all tasteful and perfect for her build, colouring

29

and age. Mr Twinkling Eyes, on the other hand, is on the short, rotund side, hair badly cut, his belly hanging over his belt, almost comical standing next to his genuinely elegant wife. Until that cheeky grin appears and those eyes twinkle, and then you forget what he looks like. His personality is as big as his wife is tall.

They tell us they have been married for forty seven years. I say that means that their marriage is officially heritage listed. The twinkle appears, he looks up and says, "Does that mean we are a crumbling pile of stones in need of serious renovation?" His wife chuckles softly. I comment how much I love the Canadian accent, to which Mr Twinkling Eyes replies, "Accent? We don't have an accent. But yours is nice." Yes, this couple will be a pleasure to travel with.

Mr and Mrs Twinkling Eyes move away and we turn to the couple behind us. American. And a little odd. Whereas Mrs Effusive was nearly jumping out of her skin with excitement, this lady is a bundle of jittery nerves and I'm not sure why. She is a strange looking woman, there is no other way of saying it. Short, wide and over blown. She's had some work done on her face, but not her neck, so the wrinkled sun-damaged turkey neck and her liver-spotted hands give her away. The hands always give a woman away. She's closer to 70 than to 60. Her hair is bleached so white it almost glows in the dark, and cut in the style one would expect on a fifteen year old - short and cropped over one ear, then long over the other ear and hanging over one eye. Her makeup is almost as white as her hair, with streaks of pink blusher along each cheekbone, thick black eyeliner around each eye and bright pink lipstick. She is wearing a pink outfit that is so busy that I can't make head or tail of it. I think it's a top and three-quarter stretch leggings, but there are ruffles, pleats, bows and frills all over the place. And then I see her shoes. High towering platform heels in patent white, her little fat feet jammed into them with toe cleavage bulging over the front of them.

As we introduce ourselves, she moves towards us and teeters so badly that Hubby and I almost reach out to support her, but withdraw quickly when we see her husband's hand gripping hers to steady her. He's a good deal younger than she is, very staid and rather plain compared to her. A curious combination.

Mrs Teetering Heels tries to make conversation, but it is disjointed by her grunts and sighs as she struggles to retain her balance. Mr Teetering Heels is clearly used to this as he adjusts his posture to balance hers and keep her upright. It's quite a sight. As Mrs Teetering Heels seems to be having trouble finishing her sentences, I address Mr Teetering Heels, but his responses are restricted to single words. His concentration is diverted to preventing his wife from falling.

Me. "Where are you from?"

Him. "San Francisco."

Me. "Retired?"

Him. "Mmm."

Me. "What did you do before you retired?"

Him. "Tax consultant."

Me. "And your wife?"

Him. "Secretary."

Me. "And is this your first trip?"

Him. "No."

Nothing more. I give up.

Mrs Teetering Heels attempts to enter the conversation in jerks and spasms. "We ... umm ... but ... ahh ... this time ... errr ... and ... umm ..."

Her voice is high pitched, squeaky and rather sweet, like a young girl's and there is something rather innocent about her. I sense there is a lovely lady underneath all that paint and decoration, but I can feel my blood pressure rising as I watch her trying to get a sentence out. It's like standing too close to a nervous tick. She's making me feel edgy.

Suddenly, Mrs Teetering Heels looks desperate, spins around and starts to stagger away, her husband using all his strength to keep her from toppling over. She moves those little tortured feet in those skyscraper heels about an inch at a time and I wonder if she'll make it in time. I recognise an Old Fart bladder alert when I see one. But she's not going to disgrace herself in company, no way! She sets her jaw and ignores the pain as they head towards the Ladies Room. I sigh with relief as they reach the Ladies Room door, where he lets her go to make her own way.

Then I notice with horror that the back of Mrs Teetering Heels' fussy top is split from the waist to the hip, exposing her rear end, and that she has the biggest, most unattractive bum I've ever seen, tightly encased in rather sheer pink stretch leggings, with her white old lady undies showing underneath and a VPL that looks like a ridge across the tops of both her legs. And I can see the outline of her incontinence pad. It is not a pretty sight. Oh dear.

I feel suddenly protective towards Mrs Teetering Heels. Her innocence is showing. I want to dash across the room and pull her top across her bum, but that would draw everyone's attention to it. So I stay where I am, hope that no one else has noticed and watch her make it to the Ladies Room. She holds onto the wall, opens the door and moves slowly forward. The struggle almost brings tears to my eyes.

Hubby leans in to me and whispers sympathetically, "Mutton dressed as lamb." That's an understatement! This is a woman who looks in the mirror and still sees her younger self. And what works on a 16 year does not work on a 60+ Old Fart. Not ever.

Then a quiet male voice says in my left ear, "I thought she wasn't going to make it for a moment there." I turn to see a gentle, intelligent face under grey hair, with serious blue eyes behind large glasses. His words could have been unkind, but they were said without malice. His wife is next to him, slim like him and modestly dressed with short wavy brown hair. She says, equally quietly, "But she did. Thank goodness." They smile, and so do we. We discreetly change the subject to talk about the chaotic Cairo traffic and the husband says, "Yes, they asked me sort it out, but I was busy designing the sports stadium for the London Olympics and couldn't make it." We chuckle.

Hubby says, "Don't worry, they asked me when you weren't available, so all was well."

Mr Gentle Wit says, "I'm glad to hear it. That leaves me free to finish revising Webster's dictionary."

Hubby responds with, "I had to turn that down. Too busy translating my wife's books into Swahili."

Mr and Mrs Gentle Wit are delightful. Both genteel and unassuming in their dress, their conversation is intelligent and fun. We learn that they are from Perth, he is a retired lawyer and she a retired financial advisor. He and Hubby understand each other's humour perfectly and so begins an ongoing conversation that endures for the whole trip. Mr and Mrs Intelligentsia would be very impressed indeed, if a single word of it was true. But then, they wouldn't get that gentle, witty banter anyway.

At that moment, a lady comes up to us and asks, in a very educated American accent, "Have you seen my husband?" She is a plump, grey haired lady wearing very expensive clothes and with a calm expression on her face.

I say, "What does he look like?"

"Can't miss him," she answers quickly, "he's wearing red pants."

Red pants? Does she mean underpants or trousers?

Mr Gentle Wit points through the crowd and asks, "Is that him?" We all turn to look and see a tall, grey haired man standing at the end of the drinks table, unmistakable in his white shirt, bright red cargo pants and red sneakers. Despite the attire, there is something distinguished about him.

Mrs Red Pants looks visibly relieved. "Thank goodness! I thought I'd lost him again."

Hubby says, "Again?"

"Oh, he's always wandering off. Early Alzheimer's, you see. That's why I make him wear red pants all the time. It's like a cat bell. I can always find him in a crowd." She looks across the room at him. "He's off with the fairies at the moment, poor darling, but when he's lucid again, I'll introduce him." She dashes across the room to his side.

This is something new. We have not struck fellow passengers with diagnosed dementia before. Most Old Farts stop travelling overseas once that diagnosis is confirmed. I wonder if they are doing this trip while they can, while Mr Red Pants is still in the manageable stage of his disease. At our age, we never know what is around the corner tomorrow or next week and we need to make the most of every day we have.

We watch them for a moment as Mr Red Pants pours champagne from one glass into another, then back into the first, then again into the other glass, over and over, with the concentration and diligence of a four year old. Mrs Red Pants stands patiently by his side, waiting for him to return to her. They have our sympathy. It could be any of us.

We talk about Alzheimer's with Mr and Mrs Gentle Wit for a few moments. No Old Fart is untouched by it, either personally or through family or friends. It's a reality that we all have the potential to face at any time and we are grateful for this moment when we are not confronted with it ourselves. Or are we? Would we know if we were? That's one of the tricky things about Alzheimer's. It's often someone else who notices the first changes.

We toast our good health and Mr and Mrs Gentle Wit move onto to Mr and Mrs Twinkling Eyes. I see the four of them laughing after the first few words of introduction. I have a feeling we'll be spending a lot of time with those four.

We look around us. We appear to have done the married couples. We have learned from previous group trips that, for some reason, when first mingling, the married couples seem to gravitate to each other and single people mingle with other single people, whether they are travelling with a companion or alone. It's not intentional. It just happens that way.

But we are mistaken. We have one more couple to meet. They approach us and begin an easy, friendly conversation. We learn that they are from New York and one is a theatre set designer and the other a casting agent. The arts! Right up my alley. I love theatre and anything associated with it. We talk briefly about the latest productions showing in

New York and in Australia and discover they are almost the same. I see rather new looking wedding rings on their fingers and ask how long they have been married. They laugh and tell us that they were married in spirit forty years ago, but only in law recently, as gay marriage was still a hot subject politically. And this is their honeymoon! Mr and Mr Gay Couple. We congratulate them.

Mr Gay Man 1, the theatre set designer, is tall and thin and very fashionably dressed, his luxuriant grey hair combed back off his handsome face. He is gracious and well spoken. Mr Gay Man 2, the casting agent, is short, flabby and wearing a flowery shirt, baggy shorts and grey socks under open sandals. He is almost bald, but what little hair he has left is tied back in a long, grey pony-tail. And he is laying on the camp behaviour just a bit too much. But we know why. He's testing us. After a few minutes of conversation, he settles down. We have passed the test. No bigots here. Hubby and I have gay friends and gay relatives. Gay, straight, black, white, Christian, Muslim, pink with purple polka dots, we don't care, just as long as people are good to each other and the sex is between consenting adults.

Mr and Mr Gay Couple settle in to an educated, witty and friendly conversation and we look forward to their company. Having passed their test, they soon move on from us to Mr and Mrs Socially Superior. I see Mrs Socially Superior suppress a look of horror when Mr Gay Man 2 waves a limp wrist at her and speaks too loudly in his camp voice. I guess they don't have a lot of married gay couples in the small Tasmanian town she comes from. Or at least, not part of her "Social Set" anyway.

I'd love to stay and watch the fun, but we are being approached by the first of the single travellers. Three women who look so much alike that, at first, I think we are speaking to triplets. Then I realise that one has dark hair, one has dark hair peppered with grey, and the third has grey hair peppered with dark. They are sisters aged 60, 65 and 70, Canadian and delightful. All three are short, neckless, round and have such cheerful dispositions that it's impossible not to smile in their presence. They all wear boxy shirts, baggy three quarter trousers flapping above fat ankles and un-pedicured feet safely encased in sensible orthopaedic sandals. Normally, I don't like this look, but somehow it works on them. One wouldn't expect any less when shaped the way they are.

They tell us that they have been planning this trip for ten years, their children have all grown and flown, they are all grandmothers now and they have all left their husbands at home to fend for themselves for six weeks. This trip is for them, a dream come true that they have saved hard for. And their passion is shopping! They have brought only one suitcase between them with a few basics, but intend to go home with six suitcases jammed full of goodies. Wow! I like shopping too, but I am truly impressed by the commitment and passion of the Shopping Sisters. Shopping Sister 1 (the youngest) shows me the two rings she has already found time to buy at the hotel jewellery shop. Shopping Sister 2 (the middle sister) is wearing a silk scarf she bought at the hotel boutique. And Shopping Sister 3 (the eldest) is wearing lapis lazuli scarab earrings she bought at the hotel souvenir shop. And they only arrived an hour ago. These gals don't waste any time! I will watch them with great interest.

Hubby, on the other hand, looks at me with concern. He hopes the Shopping Sisters aren't a bad influence. A bad influence? Are you kidding? I'm my own bad influence when it comes to shopping on holiday. It's part of the fun. But it's a girl thing. And the boys will never understand. It's just the way it is.

When the Shopping Sisters realise they have another sister in me, we discuss what we like to buy. My passion is scarves and bangles, especially Indian glass bangles and anything that glitters. Hubby tells them he calls me the Jingle Jangle Bangle Lady. I like to rattle a bit when I walk. They get it and they approve. A bond is sealed between the Shopping Sisters and myself. We chink glasses and move on.

A loud voice heralds us. Female. American. "And where do you come from?" She is standing with another woman. They are both in their mid 60's and about as bland and frumpy as you can get. In fact, when I look away, I can't picture them. Just a beige space where they should be. Which fascinates me. How can you live for so many years and be so bland? Shouldn't you pick up some sort of eccentricity in that time? Maybe their physical blandness is their eccentricity.

"We're from Canberra." Hubby replies.

"Oh, I know where that is!" she says in her ear shattering voice. At least that part of her is not bland. "It's your National Capital! It's a suburb of Sydney!"

Not bad, but wrong. Most Americans have never heard of Canberra and think Sydney is our National Capital. I correct her gently. "It's a separate city in a separate state about three hours drive out of Sydney. And where are you from?"

She and her friend look at me as if I'm stupid. Did I really need to ask? Wasn't it obvious? "Texas! Houston, to be precise!" Of course. Silly me.

Now, here's an interesting observation. We had picked Mr and Mr Gay Couple as a gay couple upon sight. But both Hubby and myself instinctively assume these Texan Gals are just friends, not a couple. The difference isn't always clear, but it seems so to us with these two. And we are right.

Texan Gal 1 continues to yell at me. "And what do you both do?"

"My husband is a retired IT consultant and I'm a writer."

"A writer!" I wonder if she always speaks with exclamation marks. "I'm a librarian! I'll know you! What have you written?"

I give her my card. She hands it to Texan Gal 2, who immediately pulls out her iPhone and Googles me, then hands the results back to Texan Gal 1.

"E-books?" Texan Gal 1 looks up at me disapprovingly. "Not real books then!"

"E-books are real books," I say in my defence, trying to suppress a grin. "Millions of people read e-books. In fact, last year, they sold more e-books than paper books. It's the way of the future."

"Well, I don't like it! We don't like it, do we?" she asks of her companion.

"No. We like the feel and smell of a paper book," Texan Gal 2 replies quietly.

I hear this a lot from our generation. I ask gently, "Do you buy a book to read it, or to smell it?"

They look a little taken aback. "To read it, of course!" Texan Gal 1 says.

Then Texan Gal 2 adds, "I'm a teacher. My students all have e-readers and tablets ..."

Texan Gal 1 exclaims, "Oh, the drugs, the drugs!"

"No, dear," her friend corrects gently, "tablets are iPads. You know, like my iPhone, but bigger."

"You mean those things you have to swipe with your fingers all the time?"

"Yes, dear."

"You'll never see me with one of those!"

"I know, dear."

I say, "Our generation are a bit resistant to change, and the changes are happening so fast now that it's hard for anyone to keep up with them."

"You're telling me!" Texas Gal 1 almost screams. "I refused to use computers and they made me retire! Me! No one knows books better than me! What can a computer do better than me? Tell me that!"

Texas Gal 2 says, "You're a dinosaur, dear. That's why they made you retire."

I almost gasp. How would Texas Gal 1 take that? She looks at her friend without offence and says, "They made you retire too!"

"Yes, but that's because I turned 65 and it was time for me to retire."

"Humph!"

"It was time for both us to retire." Texas Gal 2 pats her friend reassuringly on the arm, then looks at me. "I'll check out your books."

Hubby is curious. These women clearly know each other well. "Is this your first trip together?"

Texas Gal 1 opens her mouth to exclaim something, but Texas Gal 2 puts a gently restraining hand on her arm and replies instead. "Oh, no. We travel together every year."

I ask, "So you've known each other awhile?"

"Since primary school. We've been best friends since we were five."

"That's lovely!"

"Well, it's been a comfort. We've never married and we only live a couple of blocks from each other." Texas Gal 2 is as sweet and engaging as Texas Gal 1 is loud and irritating.

Texas Gal 1 declares, "We should move in together! I keep telling her that! Sell our old houses and get one of those nice condos! But she won't do it!"

I ask as innocently as possible. "Oh? Why not?"

"She says she'd be too hard to live with!" Texas Gal 1 looks at her gentle friend doubtfully. "But I reckon I could cope with her!"

Texas Gal 2 smiles at Texas Gal 1 and says, "I snore, dear. Very loudly. It simply wouldn't work." She's superb! She's had over sixty years practice in handling her rather loud, insensitive friend and she does it with genuine love and respect. I wonder if Texas Gal 1 knows how lucky she is.

Suddenly, Texas Gal 1 exclaims, "Look at that man!" We turn to look. Mr Red Pants is holding out the elasticated waist band of his red pants and, with lightning speed, empties a full bottle of champagne down his front. We hear him say, "Cool," as the champagne runs down his legs and forms a puddle around his feet. Mrs Red Pants grabs the bottle, puts it on the table and leads her dripping husband out of the room like a parent with a small child. His eyes are wide and empty as he passes us. I can see the resigned patience on her face. It would be funny if it wasn't so sad. Dementia is no laughing matter. Nobody says a word. After all, it could be any one of us any day now.

Then Texas Gal 1 suddenly lowers her voice and whispers hoarsely, "He's a retired history professor, you know. And she used to own one of the biggest boutiques in Boston. Worth a lot of money. But what's money when you've lost your marbles?" She shakes her head dramatically. "He'd better stay away from me!"

"Why?" Texas Gal 2 asks in her soft, tempered voice. "He's harmless, dear. He's only a danger to himself. I think we should all treat him with great kindness."

Hubby says, "Hear, hear."

Texas Gal 1 looks at Hubby, confused. Is he having a go at her? No, he's not. He's merely agreeing with Texas Gal 2, who now holds up her empty glass and says, "One more before dinner, dear?" Then she deftly leads her friend away toward the drinks table. She has good instincts.

For a moment, we are free. I look at Hubby. "What do you think so far?"

He grins. "You're going to have a ball, aren't you?"

"Don't I always?" We look around us. There is a gaggle of single ladies at the end of the drinks table. Seven of them. We have about half an hour before dinner begins, so we make our way over to them and introduce ourselves.

They are an interesting mix. The first one to respond to our introductions is a very tall, very fat and very loud fellow Australian. She reminds me of Hattie Jaques in the Carry On movies. Her thin, short hair is died a bright auburn and large, cheap earrings scrape her shoulders. I can see dye marks on the scalp. A home job done just before she got on the plane. I hope she's brought some more with her, otherwise she's going to have some interesting contrasting roots by the end of the six weeks. I can see a bit she missed behind her left ear. Silvery grey.

Within a few minutes, we have learned she is divorced, has three children and nine grandchildren with two great grandchildren on the way (and she's only in her early 60's, well done!), spent her entire working life as a nurse and midwife at the Broken Hill Hospital, the last ten years as the DON (which I explain to Hubby means Director Of Nursing, the modern term for a hospital matron, making her even more Hattie Jaques-ish) and she hates men! She seems oblivious to the fact that my Hubby is a man. Maybe other women's husbands don't count as men. To some extent, I understand that. Between husbands of my own, I had a strict rule when dating that any man who was married, engaged or involved was strictly off limits. I didn't see them as "men" either, in the terms of them being available. But whereas I set those parameters for my own protection, Ms Fat 'n Loud is just plain bitter.

She is quickly joined in her "all men are bastards" tirade by a small, sour faced woman, also another Australian from Adelaide, a retired public servant, but instead of being bitter, this one is just plain miserable. Her ex-husband ripped her off, her other relationships took advantage of her, the Global Financial Crisis was all designed to make life hard for her and her alone, the air conditioning in the room is too cold, the champagne is too warm, and so on and so forth. Ms Miseryguts. The perpetual victim. She would be exhausting if it wasn't for Miss Know-it-all.

Yessiree, our Californian Miss Know-it-all has a solution for every one of Ms Miseryguts' problems. Ripped off by an ex-husband? Get yourself a good lawyer. Trouble with your relationships? Get a good analyst. Disadvantaged by the GFC? Get a good financial advisor. The room is too cold? Put on a cardy. The champagne is too warm? Complain to the waiter.

And for every solution that Miss Know-it-all has, Ms Miseryguts has a comeback of her own. Couldn't afford a good lawyer. Can't afford a good analyst. Can't afford a good financial advisor. (So how can she afford this expensive trip?) The cardy is in her room and it is too much bother to get it. And she doesn't like the look of the waiters. They are...wait for it...foreign. Can't trust foreigners. And all this in a whining, nasal voice that is like fingernails on a blackboard.

Miss Know-it-all eventually rolls her eyes and turns away from Ms Miseryguts, who feels the slight and adds it to her list of miseries. There is no winning with that one.

We learn Miss Know-it-all is a retired kindergarten teacher from Los Angeles, unmarried but not a virgin (yes, she said that) and has no self esteem issues at all. More of us should be like her (yes, she said that too). She isn't into problems, she's into solutions. And she loves to quote statistics. Like "did we know that 50% of the Egyptian economy relies on tourism?" Actually, we did know that. It was on one of the sites we researched when preparing for this trip. But Miss Know-it-all firmly believes that she is the only one with facts like this at her fingertips. I like her. Actually, I like Ms Fat 'n Loud and Ms Miseryguts too. They all add to the colour of this cross section of Old Farts.

Amongst the single women are two much older ladies, each white haired and leaning on their walking sticks. We say hello and are welcomed with genuine warmth. They ask us about ourselves and are very interested in my writing. We learn that they are both widowed, both spent their lives on farms, one in Western Australia and the other in New South Wales and are 79 and 89 respectively. They have only just met, like us, but are drawn to each other by their seniority and their backgrounds. We love the Two Oldies on sight.

Young Oldie, who is the shorter and slightly stouter of the two, has a sadness in her eyes, a tiredness that I put down to her age and the long trip out here, but would in time discover stems from a situation at home that she has escaped from by booking this trip just a week ago. She tells us she didn't want to give anyone time to stop her, but

49

doesn't go into any more detail. It is too hard for her. Her eyes mist up and Old Oldie pokes her in the bum with her walking stick and says matter-of-factly, "None of that, now." Young Oldie smiles gratefully. Someone understands.

Old Oldie was once tall and broad shouldered, but now looks quite frail and stooped. Her white hair is thin and wispy, whereas Young Oldie's hair is a tight mat of short wiry curls. I ask Old Oldie what made her decide to come on this particular tour, as it would be quite demanding. She looks at me with a cheeky grin and says bluntly, "I'll be dead soon. I may as well be dead in an Egyptian temple or an Italian fountain or an Irish castle as in a smelly old nursing home. Figure I'll just keep living 'til it's time to die."

I say, "I'll drink to that!" and we chink glasses.

All the time we have been chatting with Ms Fat 'n Loud, Ms Miseryguts, Miss Know-it-all and the Two Oldies, there has been a constant chatter going on in my right ear, like a cacophony of meaningless sound. I finally turn to address it.

The noise is coming from a woman about my own age and build, casually dressed, not unattractive, but with a mouth that never stops moving. I know words are coming out of it, but in such a monotonous, grating voice that I can't seem to decipher them. She doesn't seem to be addressing any of us in particular, she is just talking for the sake of talking. I put my hand on her shoulder to get her attention. She turns to me and, without missing a beat, says, "I left him at home because he doesn't like to travel."

"Left who at home?" I ask.

"My husband, of course. He doesn't like to travel, you see, but he likes me to do what I enjoy, so I book a trip every year. Sometimes just to see one of our children. They all live away, you see. We're in Ottawa. Our son lives in Winnipeg. Our eldest daughter lives in Edmonton. Our youngest daughter lives in Regina ..."

"You're Canadian?" I try to enter the conversation but she continues as if I haven't spoken.

"... and my husband travels a lot with his work. He could retire, but he keeps putting it off. I visit the children every year and travel overseas every second year. My husband is a very generous man. He always pays for my trips away. I can't, you see, I'm just a housewife. But I'm very busy. I have my garden club and I do ..."

Mrs Love-a-chat is still talking. I know that because her mouth is still moving, but it's like I have entered the twilight zone. I've tuned out. And then I see that, although she is facing me, her eyes are not making contact with me. In fact, she seems to be looking inward. And I'm not surprised that her husband pays for her to go away every year, and that he continues to work in a job that takes him away from home, rather than retire and spend all his time at home with his never-silent wife. She is relentlessly boring.

I pull myself up short. No one is boring. Everyone has a story. Especially Old Farts. The older the Old Fart, the better their stories. Mrs Love-a-chat is like she is for a reason. I'll hear her story and find that reason, but not right now. I'm still a bit jet lagged and don't have the energy.

As I've already said, I am not impolite, but I feel trapped. I turn away a little. She doesn't notice. I turn away some more. She continues to chat relentlessly. I turn my back on her. She is completely unaware that I have shut her out.

With relief, I turn to Hubby who is engaged in conversation with a very fit, almost athletic looking woman in her mid 60's. Canadian, with a strong, deep voice. She has an androgynous look to her, with hair cut very short, no makeup or jewellery and is wearing loose linen trousers and a t-shirt under a travel vest. I recognise the travel vest, as I have one myself, a clever article of clothing that looks like a sleeveless vest from the outside, but has many pockets and compartments on the inside to keep all of one's money, documents and valuables in. The most secure way of carrying all the things you need when you travel. It comes with sleeves that can be zipped on and worn in cooler climates. I have used mine on several trips. The only reason I haven't brought mine this trip is that we have "dress dinners" nearly every night on this trip and I decided I wanted a change from my usual travel uniform of jeans, t-shirts, travel vest, jackets and trainers. So I purchased a black anti-theft travel bag that will double as a handbag at the dinners, and packed some "nice" clothes for the evenings, as well as the usual hardy and comfortable day clothes.

Hubby is deep in conversation about Cornwall and this lady is a wealth of information. We are planning to do some ancestor hunting while we are in England, hire a car on our free day and visit some of the villages in Cornwall that my family came from a hundred and fifty years ago. She has been to Cornwall several times and when I tell her the names of the villages, she is familiar with all of them. We learn that she started out as a teacher, then discovered that she could make more money being a private tutor to rich Canadian families wanting to get their children into the right colleges and universities. She could choose when she worked and when she took time off. She told us she was from a large family of thirteen children, her father had died when she was ten and her mother had suffered much hardship raising her big family, which made Miss Well Travelled decide that marriage and children were not for her. So as she worked and made money, she invested some in property and the rest in travel. There isn't much of the world she hadn't seen, and now her investment properties are making her a good living and she travels most of the time.

I ask her why this tour. She says it isn't safe for a woman her age to travel alone any longer. She'd been mugged recently in Spain and robbed in Thailand, so she travels with groups now, and she liked this particular company because they use new buses with seats that have extra leg room (she is rather tall), not too many people per tour, and four and five star accommodation. And yes, Miss Well Travelled has been to all the destinations of this trip before, several times in fact, but she says she never tires of seeing things more than once. It is better than staying at home in her apartment, wondering what to do with herself. She's quite a lady!

The dinner gong is sounded and we all make our way into the dining room. It is rather grand, with chandeliers and crystal and marble. We are ushered to a long table that looks like something straight out of Buckingham Palace.

We take our seats. And there we are. All thirty-one of us middle class, white, western English-speaking Old Farts.

Mrs and Mrs Socially Superior, Mr and Mrs Intelligentsia, Mr and Mrs Twinkling Eyes, Mr and Mrs Effusive, Mr and Mrs Teetering Heels, Mr and Mrs Gentle Wit, Mr and Mrs Red Pants (they have returned with him dried off and in fresh red pants, but he still looks off with the fairies), Mr and Mr Gay Couple, the 3 Shopping Sisters, the 2 Texan Gals, Ms Fat 'n Loud, Ms Miseryguts, Miss Know-it-all, the Two Oldies, Mrs Love-a-chat (who is still talking to herself), Miss Well Travelled - and us, the Jingle Jangle Bangle Lady and Hubby. And of course, our tour guide, Leslie. Which makes thirty-one.

Leslie stands and welcomes us formally. She tells us she has been a tour guide for fifteen years, has done all of Europe and most of the Asian and Middle Eastern countries, has an Arts degree majoring in European history, a Bachelor of Languages majoring in Italian, now speaks seven languages fluently and loves her job. We are impressed. She reads out our list of names and nationalities and we obediently put up our hands as our names are heard. And like the pro she is, from that moment on she remembers each and every one of us by our names. Which is more than I can do.

Remembering names is one of my biggest failings, always has been. You can tell me your name is Sally or John twenty times and I won't remember (unless I gave birth to you or my mother did), but I never forget a personality. Never! Which is why I remember people by their nature or eccentricity or talent. Hubby is used to it and knows who I am talking about when I mention someone. I think he is just grateful that I remember his name. Although I call him "darling" a lot. He'll catch on one day.

Leslie gives us the mandatory instructions about luggage, tipping, timetables, seat rotation on the buses and, of course, personal security which includes warnings about thieves and pickpockets. She then gives us her mobile number, which we all dutifully enter into our own mobiles, and passes around a sheet for us to write our mobile numbers on, which she enters into her own mobile during the course of the evening.

Someone sitting close to her comments on the very beautiful engagement ring she is wearing and asks when the big day is. Leslie smiles, her eyes lighting up, and says, "Two weeks after this tour ends."

Well, that begins a whole other conversation. Not with the men, but with the women. We all want to know about her fiancé (he's a tour company manager), how long they've been engaged (a year), where they are getting married (Rome, because her fiancé is Italian), where they are going on their honeymoon (nowhere, because they travel all the time and four weeks at home is a holiday for them both) and where they live (Tuscany). We love her and are very happy for her. And all the while we are having this delightful conversation, I notice that her handbag is hanging off the back of her chair, unzipped, and her wallet is sticking out of the top of it. I want to tell her, but don't because, after all, she is an experienced tour guide and after telling us all the do's and don'ts of securing our valuables, she must know what she is doing.

Our meal is wonderful. The wine is excellent. The conversation is affable. Mostly. Mrs Socially Superior is the exception. She has sunk into a state of gloom, picks at her food and talks to no one. After a few attempts to draw her into the general conversation, we all give up and leave her to her own devices. Her husband, on the other hand, is very jovial and appears not to notice his wife's silence. Perhaps he is used to it.

Hubby and I retire to our room around 9pm and are both in bed by 9.30pm. Our normal bed time and, I suspect, the normal bedtime for most of our group.

DAY 2

THE PYRAMIDS

We are up at 6am the following morning, showered, dressed and at breakfast by 7am, as per the schedule which is put up each evening in whatever hotel we stay at. We know how it works. These "senior" tours are geared to make it as easy as possible for us. One of the great things about being an Old Fart on a good package tour.

And everyone is on time. That's the other good thing about being an Old Fart. We've all raised children or had jobs or both, run homes or businesses or both, answered to bosses or been responsible for staff or both, taken on and successfully handled all sorts of responsibilities - and we all go to bed early. We understand schedules.

And why is this good? Well, when you are young and travel, you want to go out at night and party on dude. You drink too much, go to bed too late and wake up feeling like crap. You are still at the beginning of your responsible years and, when at home, you don't think twice about taking a sick day off work or university if you wake up with a hangover. If you wake up with a hangover while you're travelling with a tour, you drag your heels, whinge about the early mornings and make the tour guides grind their teeth while they wait for you to get your arse into gear and onto the bus. I have heard more than one tour guide say how much they enjoy Old Fart tours, as we are always on time in the mornings, never get drunk or disorderly and are tucked into bed early at night, which leaves the tour guides free to do their own thing. We are the preferred clients.

However, we do present the tour guides with other problems. But those problems aren't usually self imposed, which makes them forgivable.

We are seeing the Pyramids of Giza and The Sphinx today. After breakfast, we return briefly to our rooms to ablute, which technically means to wash oneself, but is Hubby's own special word for taking the critical morning dump. It's a necessity for Old Farts, for whom routine is health. I personally don't like to start the day without brushing my teeth as well.

We have dressed for the heat. Hubby in his cotton t-shirt, shorts and sandals and me in light linen trousers and shirt, but not sandals. I wear my trainers and cotton socks on day trips, regardless of the weather. I learned the hard way about sunburnt feet many years ago. Even with liberal amounts of sunscreen, I still burn at the merest hint of sun. Which is why I have the big floppy-brimmed bowler's hat on. And a parasol.

When we were in Japan a few years ago, I saw the Japanese women carrying parasols everywhere. It gives more protection than a hat and can be angled towards the sun as it moves across the sky during the day. I never travel without one now. And I see that western women are catching on. A friend of mine has even opened her own parasol business and it's doing well. She gave me the latest model, which has the underside of the flowery parasol lined with insulation. Amazingly simple, but incredibly cool, especially in the Egyptian sun. A good idea is always a good idea.

But hats and parasols can't protect my fair skin against wind burn and I'd been warned about the gritty wind in Egypt, so I am extremely grateful to see that this fine May day is calm and relatively mild. Only 35 degrees in the shade today. Very

Australian and no problem for me at all. After all, I was born in an Australian heat wave. Hubby, on the other hand, was born in a Scottish winter and feels the heat a lot more, but he's not the complaining sort, so we just get on with it.

I washed my short grey bob this morning, but didn't bother to dry or style it. I've travelled in the heat before. It makes no difference what you do with your hair in the heat. It air dries very quickly, you jam it under a hat and at the end of the day, it looks the same, no matter what you did with it that morning. As I mentioned before, hat hair is hat hair.

And no makeup today. Makeup is a big mistake in the heat. I'm not bothered by how I look. No one looks at me anyway. One of the great advantages of being a plain Old Fart. I used to wish I was prettier when I was young, but as I grew older, I realised I had less to lose, and actually think my face is more interesting with a few lines on it now. Like a good wine, I get better with age. Well, that's my story and I'm sticking to it.

As we climb aboard the bus, I notice Mrs Socially Superior ahead of me. Unlike me and most of the other women this morning, she has taken great care with her appearance. Her hair is teased and smoothed, she is hatless, her makeup applied with a palette knife and she is wearing another beige polyester top, black elastic waisted polyester pants and black ballet flats. Blimey. She's going to be slithering around inside that makeup and those clothes before long! I hope she's super-glued those false eyelashes on.

I hear a clatter behind me and glance over my shoulder. Mrs Teetering Heels is coming towards us. Teetering. This time on backless high-heeled sandals. Didn't she hear Leslie tell us last night to wear good walking shoes? Well, maybe that's what she considers good walking shoes. I guess it's all in the eye of the beholder. Her husband is helping her along with his accustomed iron grip on her arm. At least she's wearing cotton. A little cotton, anyway. A very short, tight white t-shirt stretched across her voluminous bust with "I Love Egypt" written on the front, barely covering the lacy bra underneath, and tight white trousers that come to just below the knee. She's a series of rolling bulges from neck to knee and looks remarkably like the Marshmallow Man from the Ghostbusters movie. From the front, she's almost as bad as from the back. My heart goes out to her.

Hubby and I take our seats and I watch as the others board. Most of us are suitably dressed for the day. Even though I'm not a fan of the de-feminising Suburban Blob Hairdo, I can certainly see its advantages at times like this. Shower, comb and you're ready for the day. A hat, no hat, makes no difference. It always stays neat and tidy. There are lots of three quarter trousers and sensible sandals to be seen on the women, and most of the men, like my Hubby, are in cargo shorts and good leather sandals.

Except for Mr Red Pants. He's wearing his trademark full length red cargo pants and expensive red trainers. As he and Mrs Red Pants board the bus and move towards the back seat, he smiles and nods at each of us. "Hello." "Good morning." "Lovely day." "How are you?" We nod, smile and acknowledge the greeting as he passes by. What a difference! Last night he was a small innocent child. Today we see an intelligent, educated and charming man. Mrs Red Pants looks relaxed and very happy indeed. They take their place at the very back of the bus.

And then I see Mrs Twinkling Eyes approaching the bus. She is already wearing a hat, straw, wide upturned brim, very chic. She must have bought it here in Egypt because it would crush in a suitcase. Her short hair has been fluffed a little around the edges of the hat, softly framing her lovely face. The makeup is perfect with a light dusting of powder, a little mascara and lip gloss.

But! She has broken the cardinal rule for women over 60 - she is wearing shorts. I can't believe it! She seemed so stylish last night. The shorts are black, very slimming and come to just above her knees. And then I see that she has an amazing pair of pins under those shorts. Smooth, evenly tanned, great calves, slender ankles, no veins or moles or stubble, and she has perfectly pedicured blue toenails with flowers painted on them. Flowers! I am truly impressed. I tell her so as she and her husband take their seats directly opposite us.

"You've got a great pair of pins there," say I.

She looks down at her linen blouse. "Oh, dear, did the dry cleaners leave some pins in my blouse?"

I laugh. "No, your legs. You have a great pair of legs."

She grins at me. "Why, thank you!"

Mr Twinkling Eyes leans across, pats his wife's knees and says rather lustfully, "And they're all mine." We chuckle.

The 2 Texan Gals get to the bus. Suddenly, Texan Gal 1 stops and cries, "Oh no, not steps!"

I lean forward to see what the problem is. There are three steps inside the bus. We have all traversed them without problem, although Mrs Teetering Heels took her time, but Texan Gal 1 seems frozen with fear at the sight of them. Texan Gal 2 takes her by the elbow and says gently, "It's alright, dear. Just hold onto the rail and you'll be fine." Texan Gal 1 obeys and boards the bus. Very strange indeed.

Everyone is aboard now. Then Leslie gets onto the bus, followed by a very good looking young Egyptian man wearing a white cotton galabeya. What we called a kaftan back in the seventies. We've seen a lot of men wearing them since we arrived here. He looks like a tall glass of cool water. She stands at the front of the bus as we get going and introduces him.

"This is Mohamed. He will be with us for the duration of the Egyptian stage of our tour. Mohamed is Cairo born and bred and has a degree in Egyptology, as do all the Egyptian tour guides with our company. He will be assisting me in explaining the mysteries of ancient Egypt to you."

We, the female Old Farts, are well pleased. We may be over 60, but we still enjoy a bit of eye candy and Mohamed is a gourmet sweet. He smiles at all of us and takes the microphone as Leslie sits down. I notice she looks a little tired. Well, she is English and it is hot, I'm not really surprised.

"Good morning," Mohamed says with a rather delicious Arabic accent. He proceeds to give us the tourist spiel about Cairo as we drive through it towards Giza.

Cairo is fascinating, about as different from our modern home city of Canberra as can be imagined. Hubby and I hang on his every word. And I snap away madly through the bus window. My techno savvy husband bought me a new super fast camera before we left for this trip. A Point And Click camera. It finds the focus, the lighting, frames the picture and all sorts of things I don't understand, but basically means I just raise the camera in the general direction of what I want to photograph and click, and it takes the most magical photos. I used to have the old fussy cameras that you have to adjust before taking a shot, but not with this one. I love it! Hubby has decided to try his new iPhone for videoing today instead of the video camera, which means we can both take photos and videos with gadgets that fit in our pockets. Too easy.

The other members of the tour who, like us, are here for the first time are also doing a lot of pointing and clicking with a variety of expensive gadgets. We are very excited. Those who have been here before, like Miss Well Travelled, sit back and simply enjoy the ride.

I notice three of our tour members are coughing. The mandatory tour bus lurgy. It can't be avoided. It only takes one tour member to have a cold or, even worse, gastro, and it sweeps through the tour like wildfire. There is no escape, being in an enclosed space with the air conditioning spreading the bugs faster than if you went right up to the coughing person and French kissed them. Hubby and I were caught unprepared on our first tour, but we have come fully equipped on this tour. Cough syrup, decongestant, a Ventolin inhaler, nasal spray, pseudoephedrine, paracetamol, and lozenges. And for the gastro, we have electrolytes and anti-diarrhoea medication.

And let's not forget the antibiotics we bought at the Cairo airport pharmacy. Over the counter antibiotics which were recommended to us by our doctor at home to deal with the inevitable Cairo Tummy. You don't need a prescription for them here in Egypt. She also gave us a pamphlet advising us not to drink the water in Egypt, as it was laced with e-coli which the Egyptians are immune to, but which makes most tourists ill. It's bottled water all the way, with precautions taken when showering. You shower or bathe from the neck down, wash your hair separately without letting any water get on your face, brush your teeth with bottled water and wash your face with bottled water.

I take this all very seriously as my tummy is dodgy at the best of times, but Hubby, who has a steel lined gut, just keeps his mouth closed under the shower. He follows all the other rules though. And our tour company provides us with unlimited bottled water.

We are also provided with a list of rules about what to eat when away from our accommodation in Egypt. If you can peel it yourself or unpack it, it should be safe. This tour company guarantees us "Diamond Quality" food preparation for all meals they provide at our hotels and on the river cruise, but when we are out feeding ourselves, we have to be careful. Old Farts can't play around with this sort of thing. Most of us have other health issues, which can be complicated with a dose of Cairo Tummy. And who wants to be laid up with a dose of the trots when you should be out seeing some of the wonders of the world?

Some of our friends at home who have travelled to Egypt advised us to bring a few things of our own. So we packed four dozen muesli bars, several packets of savoury and sweet biscuits and a dozen bags of gelatine lollies. It seemed a bit extreme at the time, but now we realise how sensible it was. We carry a half dozen muesli bars, biscuits and lollies in zip-lock plastic bags at all times in my bag and Hubby's backpack. And we ended up needing them on those days when we were free to find our own lunch and all that was on offer was the food stall that smelled wonderful, but just plain horrified us when we saw the cooking conditions. Middle class western Old Farts are a fussy lot.

I digress again. You'll get used to that after awhile.

So. We arrive at the car park at Giza and pull up just as another bus parks next to us. I glance over at the other bus, nudge Hubby and we both groan. The name of an Australian tour group is painted across the side of the bus.

Gawd help us. It's a bus full of young Aussies.

Now, don't get me wrong. I love young Aussies. Hubby and I between us have produced a few of them ourselves, and they are now producing a few more of their own. They are all decent, well behaved, good citizens and we are proud of them all. They are fairly typical of the fine young people populating Australia.

But something happens to young Aussies, especially between the ages of 18 and 25, when they travel overseas in groups. They have a bad reputation internationally and, damn it, they deserve it. They almost pride themselves on being drunk, loud, uncouth and, in packs, terminal idiots. They aren't like that at home with their families, although maybe they can be when they are out with their mates. I remember being a terminal idiot myself when I was 17 and had just left home to start my first job. It just goes with the territory of youth. But we didn't travel overseas in packs the way they do now. We kept our idiocy within our own borders.

And we didn't have Schoolies Week back then. Schoolies Week at the end of Year 12 has gotten out of hand and a lot of new school leavers find themselves in all sorts of trouble after a week of letting their hair down just a tad too much. It's like letting thousands of caged animals out for the first time. They don't quite know how to handle their new found freedom and many of them do it rather badly. It has become an annual social disaster for many Australian communities.

We Aussie Old Farts complain a lot that Young Aussies seem to have more freedom than we did at their age. But when you come right down to it, who's to blame? Their parents, of course. And that is, unfortunately, us! Our so-called new-age, women's libber, freedom-and-equality, sexual revolution of the 60's and 70's has come back to bite us on the bum in the form of our educated, self-confident and cashed-up children and grandchildren.

Oh my, I sound like my own grandmother. Finding fault with the young of our species. Never mind. Those very same young will one day be Old Farts themselves and they'll sit in judgement of their own grandchildren. It's the nature of our species.

So here we are, thirty Old Farts, with about sixty noisy young Aussies spilling out of the bus next to us. Equal numbers of boys and girls. I can see that they all fit into the 18 to 25 age group, but mostly the 18's. For the 18's, this is probably their reward for passing their Year 12 exams and possibly part of the now very fashionable Gap Year. This will be their first trip away from home, away from Mum and Dad, away from authority and rules and regulations. Most of them are strapping, healthy and attractive in their big sunglasses, sloppy tops and baggy shorts (Australians are not known for their sartorial elegance) and have already acquired tans. And they have energy to burn. You can feel it emanating from them. They are looking for action and if they don't find it, they'll create it themselves.

They are oblivious to us at first as we alight, then one of them, a tall young man, sees Hubby's golf hat with the Australian Flag emblazoned across it. He calls out, "Hey, mate! You an Aussie or just wearing that for show?"

I hiss to Hubby quickly, "Answer him in your old Scottish accent."

But too late. The young man has good hearing and upon picking up on my own Aussie accent, cries out to his comrades, "Hey, they're Aussies! Old Fart Aussies!"

As one, the group turns to us and call out friendly greetings. Over-the-top Aussie style impress-the-foreigner greetings. In Australia, they'd say, "Hello, how are you, nice to meet you." But here, it's all "G'day mate! How's ya goin'! You's having a good time? We're flat out like a lizard drinking! Hot enough to fry an egg on a bare arse, hey but!"

Then they pause, and I think, "No! Don't do it! Please don't do it!"

But, damn it, they do it.

They go into the Aussie chant at the top of their very healthy and robust voices.

"AUSSIE AUSSIE AUSSIE, OI OI OI!

AUSSIE AUSSIE AUSSIE, OI OI OI!

AUSSIE OI!

AUSSIE OI!

AUSSIE AUSSIE AUSSIE, OI OI OI!"

Our group turns to watch them. The Americans and the Canadians are amused, but we Australians cringe. Because we know what is coming next.

The young man who originally called out to us orchestrates it. He cries, "Let's show 'em how much we love them! Let's do it for the Aussie Old Farts!"

As one, all of the young men line up, turn their backs to us and drop their pants. They are mooning us! I want to rush over there and smack their disrespectful backsides. We Aussies are better than this.

Aren't we?

The American and Canadian Old Farts are stunned and amused. We Australian Old Farts, on the other hand, are not. We are still cringing.

Mrs Socially Superior turns her nose up and sneers, "Disgusting!"

Ms Miseryguts moans, "The young people of today are terrible. There's no hope for us, no hope at all."

Mrs Effusive adjusts her multifocals, inspects the row of bums and says, "Nope. None of my old students there."

Mr Intelligentsia says knowingly, "It's the lack of discipline in the home these days, that's what it is."

Miss Know-it-all adds, "They'll all end up criminals, mark my words."

Mr Gentle Wit offers his legal opinion. "Might be hard to identify them in a line up."

Mr Red Pants says, "An enviable line up, though, wouldn't you agree?"

Mr Gentle Wit agrees. "Yes. No tradie cracks there."

Hubby says, "Definitely a very educated middle class group of backsides."

A chuckle passes through our group.

Then Mrs Love-a-Chat makes her observation. "Isn't it strange how boys' bottoms don't age the same way that girls' bottoms do? We get cellulite and saggy and wrinkly, but they stay the same."

Then Old Oldie, with the wisdom and experience of 89 years, says to Mrs Love-a-Chat, "You're right. My husband was 81 when he died, but his backside still looked like two perfect peach halves, even though you had trouble finding the rest of him in amongst all the wrinkles."

Ms Fat 'n Loud grins and says, "Is that how you identified him for the death certificate?"

Old Oldie grins back and nods. "Oh yes. I'd know that backside anywhere."

We break out into laughter.

The young Aussies take our laughter as approval and the boys wiggle their bare arses at us even more. I hear one of the girls cry out, "Way to go, Tony!" She's addressing the young man who started it all.

And then my clever Hubby does something that will forever make him a hero in the eyes of our group. He steps towards the bare bums and slaps the arse of the boy who began it. "Tony!" he cries. "I'd know that little backside anywhere!"

Tony pulls his shorts up quickly and turns around, shocked. He looks at Hubby without recognition. And so he should. He has never seen Hubby before. But he doesn't know that.

Hubby continues with a big grin on his face. "How are you, my boy!" He embraces the confused young man. "Why, I used to wipe the poo off that bum of yours when you were just a baby!"

Our group of Old Farts are watching with great amusement.

Hubby says, "How are Mum and Dad? I was only talking to them a couple of weeks ago. They didn't tell me you'd be here at the same time as us. You remember my wife?" He points to me. I smile hugely and wave at Tony. "She got a great video of you all mooning us then." I hold up my camera and point at it gleefully.

Tony looks dismayed.

Hubby laughs loudly. "Oh, you guys! You are a barrel of laughs! I got a good picture, too." He holds up his iPhone. "I've just sent it to your Mum and Dad. And I'll put it up on my Facebook page right now." He makes a big deal of swiping and poking the iPhone screen a couple of times. "Done! And my wife will put the video up on YouTube tonight. What a hoot, hey? I reckon it'll go viral in no time at all. I'll tag your arse on Facebook, of course. Not everyone will recognise you otherwise, will they? And if you don't mind getting on to my Facebook page, you can tag those other fine arses, too."

Tony is looking at him with sheer horror now. The other boys have pulled their shorts up toot sweet and are gathering around him. Tony says, "You know Mum and Dad? I don't remember you ..."

Hubby grins malevolently. He's having fun. "Well, it's been awhile since we saw you. Three or four years. Or maybe five. I think you were still at primary school when we saw you last. But we've kept in touch with Mum and Dad. But hey, look at you now! What a fine young man you have become. Your Mum and Dad must be so proud." He looks across at me as if I have beckoned him, which I have not. "Oh, can't stay to chat. The missus is calling. Gotta keep up with the group. Us oldies take a bit longer to get around than you youngsters. But it's been great to see you. Have a great time. Bye for now!" He waves at the rather dismayed looking youths and returns to us.

We move away with Mohamed who had been watching with some amusement. He says to Hubby, "Do you really know that young man, sir?"

"Nah. Never saw him before in my life. But he doesn't know that, does he?"

"And did you really get a photo of ... what they did?"

"No. And I don't have a Facebook account. But let him stew about it for awhile, hey? He might think twice before he does that again."

Ms Fat 'n Loud hollers, "You should have taken a photo! Wish I'd thought of it myself!"

"I did," says Miss Well Travelled calmly. "I'll put it up on my Facebook page and say it was one of the highlights of Egypt. You breed some very nice backsides in Australia!"

Ms Miseryguts, who is a bit slow on the uptake, says, "Horrible little beasts! I hope his parents give him a good telling off!"

Miss Know-it-all says rather insensitively, "Oh, get with it! He doesn't really know that boy. He was just having a laugh!"

"Ooohhh. I see." I'm not sure that Ms Miseryguts does see, but she nods as if she understands.

Mrs Twinkling Eyes says, "At least you picked out a decent backside. The one at the other end was decidedly hairy and in need of a wax job." At which we all burst out laughing.

I glance over my shoulder. The young people are gathered around Tony, looking concerned. They haven't heard our conversation. They are too busy searching their iPhones and iPads for their naked backsides. We hear one of the other boys say, "But what if your Mum tells my Mum. Cripes, I'll cop it big time!"

We walk away, still laughing. Even Ms Miseryguts is trying to chuckle. What a great start to the day!

And the bonding has begun. There is nothing like a common enemy to unite a disparate group of people. Not that Tony and his mates are the enemy, or that we are particularly disparate, but our mutual laughter unites us as nothing else could. And we will need it on this trip, as we are to discover sooner rather than later.

We follow Mohamed towards the Sphinx. The Two Oldies hold hands and concentrate on keeping up, their walking sticks clattering on the paved path. They had both told us the night before that they were determined not to slow the group down, or to ever be the last to arrive anywhere. They needn't have worried. Mrs Teetering Heels will be the one we all have to wait for. She struggles along with her husband's vice-like grip keeping her from toppling over, huffing and puffing with the effort. He seems not to mind. Mohamed stops and waits for her to catch up, but Mr Teetering Heels quickly says, "Don't wait for us. We'll get there in our own time." Mohamed nods and takes him at his word, with a caution to be back at the bus on time, no matter what.

Behind us, I hear Texan Gal 1 complain in her, to our ears, grating accent, "Oh no! More steps!" Followed quickly by Texan Gal 2's soft reassurance.

Ms Fat 'n Loud is struggling and we've barely begun. Her weight might be an issue, but she is made of tough stuff and wheezes along behind us.

Mrs Socially Superior is also huffing and puffing, but that's because she is overheating inside her polyester prison. Her husband appears oblivious to her discomfort. In fact, he appears oblivious to her completely. I feel a little sorry for her.

I notice that Leslie has stayed with the bus. She really must be tired.

Hubby and I find ourselves strolling with Mr and Mrs Red Pants who are walking hand in hand.

Hubby introduces us properly and we shake hands. And I see that there is a little more to the linked hands of Mr and Mrs Red Pants than is at first apparent. Both are wearing leather bracelets tied together by another piece of leather about two feet long. She has got him leashed like a dog. Hubby and I pretend not to notice.

Mr Red Pants is charming. He asks Hubby how long he worked in IT. Hubby says, "Since 1963, straight out of school."

"Really?" Mr Red Pants stops. He is genuinely interested. "I'm working on the history of IT with a younger member of the faculty. It's my retirement project. We hope to get a book out of it. I don't suppose you have any photos or ..."

"Photos?" I chime in. "My husband has kept everything since the day he left school. Workplace contracts, equipment brochures, he's even got some of the original programming cards and the chads that came out of them."

"Chads?" asks Mrs Red Pants.

"The little pieces of card that are left after the programming cards have been hole punched," Hubby says.

"Noooo!" Mr Red Pants is amazed.

"And," I add, "he does have photos of all the computers he worked on from the first day."

Mr Red Pants becomes quite excited. "Would you be willing to be involved in our project?"

Hubby is chuffed. "I'd be delighted! I can dig out what I've got when we get home and send it to you. I was wondering what to do with it all, anyway. We're planning to downsize soon and we'll have to cull a lot of stuff."

Mrs Red Pants rolls her eyes. "We've just been through that. It's hell, but worth it."

"We'll need to talk. It's a pity we don't live closer," Mr Red Pants says.

"We can Skype. Not a problem." Hubby has it all worked out.

Mrs Red Pants quickly says, "I'll put you in touch with my husband's colleague on this project." She gives us a meaningful look. "Some days are better than others for research."

To which Mr Red Pants says, without any qualms, "Yes. I've got this damned Alzheimer's. My wife tells me I am quite out of it some days, but I don't remember. I only remember when I'm having a good day." He raises his hand with the leather lead attached. "She says I tend to get lost, so this is to keep track of me. We have something like this on our two year old grandson, too." He gives a good natured smile. "I suppose I'll be in diapers next."

"Well, not today dear, not today," his wife responds calmly. And we continue on our way to join the group.

Mohamed gathers us around him and tells us everything there is to know about the Sphinx. We decide we all hate Napoleon for blowing off the Sphinx's nose, and love the ancient Egyptians for building it to begin with.

Mr Twinkling Eyes remarks, "Nice pile of rocks. Heritage listed, like me and the wife."

We move on to the pyramids.

Mr Twinkling Eyes says, "Looks like another pile of rocks to me." The group members within hearing give a little chuckle.

The heat is blistering by now. It's radiating upwards off the hot white sand, as well as beating down on our hatted heads. But we want to hear every word of what Mohamed has to tell us. Hubby and I know we will not pass this way again and we don't want to miss a moment. The heat is uncomfortable, but you have to expect a bit of discomfort when you travel. And we know we can retreat to the air conditioned bus when the day is done, and our luxury hotel to nap and recuperate later.

It is midday and Mohamed tells us to get ourselves some lunch and then we have two hours to explore Giza ourselves. By now, there are thousands of tourists like us milling around. We note our meeting point for later, synchronise our watches and head off on our own.

This is the part of a group tour that Hubby and I often enjoy the most. Normally, we would stroll hand in hand, it's what we like to do, but it is just too bloody hot for that, so we make sure we stay close to each other, as it would be very easy to get separated in this crowd. We agree that if we do get separated, we will head straight back to the bus to find each other.

We wander amongst the grand ruins and the market stalls, munching on our safe muesli bars and swigging our bottled water. There is much more here than just the pyramids. We stand above the remains of the ancient town that housed those clever men who built the pyramids. The Pharaohs didn't build them. They just paid for them. It was thousands of little men with hammers and chisels and sheer brute strength who built these magnificent structures. They are the people I admire the most and the people I now pay homage to.

There is a commotion nearby. We ignore it at first, then we hear Ms Fat 'n Loud's unmistakable voice bellowing, "Get him down before he falls!" We move towards the base of the great pyramid. A crowd has gathered and everyone's faces are turned upward. We follow their gaze and gasp in genuine horror.

There above us, far far above us, is a moving dot of red. It is Mr Red Pants. He is climbing the pyramid with the agility of a much younger man. We look around and quickly find Mrs Red Pants. She is surrounded by most of our group and we join them. I marvel at how calm she looks.

The crowd is growing. Mohamed runs up and stands next to us.

And then, as if scripted for a Middle Eastern cowboy movie, two uniformed policemen on camels appear at top speed. Have you ever seen a camel run at top speed? It's quite a sight. I don't know how anyone can keep their seat on one of those things, they throw their riders around so much. But these policemen seem glued to their beasts. They push their way through the crowd and then, to everyone's horror, they take their very large semi-automatic rifles and point them at Mr Red Pants. They begin to shout at Mr Red Pants in Arabic.

Mohamed leaps into action. He gets the attention of the two policemen and convinces them to lower their weapons. We all breathe easier. Then he talks to them for a moment. He makes a motion with his hand next to his left temple that is universal, a simple enough movement that indicates that all is not well inside Mr Red Pants' head. The policemen understand. One of them makes a call on his two way radio and within minutes, several more policemen arrive, some on camel, some on motorbike, some on foot. They move us back from the pyramid, set up a barricade and allow Mrs Red Pants and Mohamed inside the barricade. And we wait.

Several of the policemen speak good English. We hear Mrs Red Pants tell them that her husband will come down if they tell him that he is a good boy and he can have a chocolate icecream when he comes down. They proceed.

We wait with some trepidation as several policemen climb up the pyramid. We can see how dangerous it is, with bits of stone clattering down the side of the pyramid as their feet dislodge it. We lift our eyes to see where Mr Red Pants is. He has stopped climbing and has seated himself on one of the square blocks high above us, looking out at the view. It must be marvellous from up there.

It takes almost an hour to reach him and bring him down. He is completely compliant and doesn't give the policemen any trouble. The crowd is huge by now. There is applause as Mr Red Pants reaches his wife, his eyes innocent and childlike. He looks hot and annoyed, though, when he sees that his wife is empty handed. He says reproachfully, "Where's my icecream?"

She sighs. "We'll get it for you now, dear. Just thank these lovely policemen for bringing you down."

"Why? It was nice up there. You can see more from up there. Why don't you come up too?" He makes as if to go back up the pyramid. Two policemen gently restrain him.

Mohamed says, "There are icecreams in that stall just over there, sir. Why don't we go there instead."

Mr Red Pants smiles sweetly and allows himself to be led away with Mrs Red Pants in tow. We hear her say to one of the policemen, "I didn't tie the knot tight enough. He just got away from me."

Mohamed stays with the other policemen to fill in the details and, doubtless, do the necessary paperwork.

Hubby and I look at each other with relief. It could have turned out a lot worse. Then Miss Know-it-all says, in her irritating but somehow honest way, "Might have been kinder if he had fallen and killed himself. Would have been over and done with, poor man." No one condemns her statement. It might indeed have been kinder to Mr Red Pants in the long run.

Young Oldie says softly, "Yes." Nothing more, but there is such sadness in that single word that I feel my heart squeeze.

We don't want to discuss it here, in front of so many strangers.

Oh dear. The mood has taken an unexpected turn.

Our trip back to the hotel is quiet. No one complains about the heat or the sunburn, not even Mrs Socially Superior, who actually looks rather ill and is slumped in her seat with a tangible black cloud of gloom around her. We are all conscious of the fact that something far more serious is going on here than her glum mood.

Mr Red Pants is sitting on the back seat between his wife and Ms Fat 'n Loud, who somehow inspires confidence in all of us. She was a nurse. She knows about these things. As long as she is with him, we know he will be safe. For a start, if he tries to escape, she's bigger than him and could sit on him to keep him from running away. We take comfort in that thought.

That evening, at dinner, Mrs Red Pants appears without her husband. She speaks to Mohamed and Leslie for a while, then takes her seat with the rest of us. While we are waiting for our first course, Leslie rises and addresses us. She indicates Mrs Red Pants.

"As you know, today's incident caused us all a great deal of anxiety. Our fellow traveller is under sedation at present, uninjured thank goodness, but it could have been much more serious. In light of what happened, his wife has suggested that they leave the tour and return home immediately. Mohamed and I feel that we should put it to the group to decide." She looks down at Mrs Red Pants. "Perhaps you would like to explain the situation?"

Mrs Red Pants rises and addresses us. She is calm as always. "My husband was diagnosed with Alzheimer's Disease a month after we booked this tour. Up until then, we thought he was getting a little forgetful, as we all do when we get older." We nod in knowing agreement. We are all a bit forgetful in one way or another these days. "We realised it was something more when he suddenly wandered out of a tutorial one day. He is on medication, but the disease seems to be progressing rather quickly. He is completely unaware of his periods of dementia and can become confused when he is suddenly lucid again and finds that he is not where he should be. However, when lucid, he understands that he has had an absence, and as long as no one has been hurt or inconvenienced, it isn't usually a problem. Except perhaps for me and our children. But today was different. He put himself and others at risk and

I believe it is time for us to go home and consider the next stage of his disease."

Ms Fat 'n Loud speaks up. "Are you talking about a secure dementia unit?"

"I am indeed. I thought we had a few years before we needed to face that, but ..."

Young Oldie suddenly stands and interrupts. Her eyes are misty and her mouth trembles a little as she speaks. "No! You should only do that when it is the last resort." Her voice becomes shaky, but she hasn't finished yet. We pay her the respect and attention she is due. "My husband had Alzheimer's and I looked after him at home for as long as possible. It was hard, very hard, but we still had our moments and I wouldn't be without those memories. I had to put him into a home when he became violent. That's the way it goes with dementia sometimes."

Old Oldie nods vigorously. "Yes," she concurs, "that's the way it goes sometimes." These two are speaking from experience.

Young Oldie continues. "When I put him in the home, my children thought I'd done a terrible thing, but then, they didn't live with us and they didn't know what went on. They still haven't forgiven me."

Mrs Red Pants was nodding now. These words were hitting home.

"And then he died," Young Oldie said. Half the group were in tears by now, me included. "And he was gone. For good. And all I've got now are my memories of the good times."

Old Oldie says, "Yes, the memories. The memories are important."

Young Oldie goes on. "If he's still having sane periods and he's not violent, you should finish this trip and make as many memories together as you can, because he'll be gone soon enough. You'll lose him before he's even dead, poor bugger. That's what happens with Alzheimer's. I reckon you should stay, and we'll all help you look after him. That's what I reckon." She sits down with a plonk.

Ms Fat 'n Loud is the first to respond. "Hear, hear! I'll help as much as I can. I've had plenty of experience."

Ms Miseryguts speaks up in her whining voice. "Ohhh no, I don't think so, not if he's crazy ..."

Before she can say another word, Miss Know-it-all stands up, directs a meaningful glare at Ms Miseryguts and snaps, "I'm all for him staying!" Ms Miseryguts is no match for Miss Know-it-all and shuts up. Miss Know-it-all then addresses the rest of us. "My mother had Alzheimer's and we kept her going as long as we could. If we all do a little to help, then it isn't much to ask. Is it?" She has tapped in to how most of us are feeling.

Then, one by one, we all agree to help Mrs Red Pants look out for her husband. We begin to discuss the disease and who in our family and friends has it or has had it, and what their experiences were. With the exception of Ms Miseryguts, who has been thankfully rendered speechless by the force of goodwill around her. She is sitting with her arms folded and her mouth twisted into a childish pout. We ignore her.

Mrs Red Pants is deeply touched and thanks us all with great sincerity, then returns to her room to watch over her husband.

And on this night, we become a family. An Old Fart package tour family. I feel very proud to be part of it.

DAY 3

THE CAIRO MUSEUM AND THE PYRAMIDS AT SUNSET

We arrive at the Cairo Museum the next morning as it opens and people are already lining up to get in. Mr and Mrs Red Pants are with us and Mr Red Pants is in fine form. Being a History Professor, this is one area he is completely at home with. As a pre-booked group, we are able to stroll past the throngs and enter straight away. Mohamed takes us around and we are spellbound by what he says and what we see. Then he leaves us to get our own lunch and wander at leisure around the museum. Out come the muesli bars and biscuits and the inevitable bottles of water.

I can't wait to get back to the floor housing the treasures from Tutankhamen's tomb. We find most

91

of our tour doing the same thing. Mrs Effusive joins me as we hang over the display cabinets of the young Pharaoh's death mask and personal possessions. Such craftsmanship, such beauty, such wealth! And we both comment on what a pity it is that the artisans who created these wonders will never be known. Again, it is the little man crouching over his creation in his dingy workshop that I am in awe of. Not the kings and queens, the rulers and conquerors. They built their wealth and their kingdoms on the backs of the poor. Mrs Effusive and I agree that there is a perverse pleasure in being able to walk around the marvels of the ancient world, peering at the most intimate details of those powerful people's lives, knowing that the "little people" like us were once forbidden such access. We feel very modern and very smug.

Finally, it is almost time to go, but not before a visit to the museum souvenir shop. And there we find most of the other women on our tour. The 3 Shopping Sisters are going berserk. Bangles, necklaces, broaches, headdresses, scarves, silver, gold - the shop is doing very well from them alone. Mrs Effusive and I settle on a lapis lazuli bangle each and a scarf in the colours of the ancient Pharaohs - lapis lazuli blue and gold. We are well pleased. Hubby is just relieved that I didn't do a

Shopping Sisters (which is a term that has since entered our vocabulary).

Mrs Socially Superior is faring better today in the airconditioned museum and shop. She and Mrs Intelligentsia are discussing the merits of silver for day wear versus gold for evening wear, each trying to outdo the other in their knowledge of the subject. Mr and Mr Gay Couple wander in and stand behind them. Suddenly, Mr Gay Man 2 leans over and says, "Of course, it was Wallis Simpson who said that one should only wear silver during the day and gold during the evening. And she married a king, so who can argue with that!" And he wanders off with a little smirk. The two women buy both gold and silver. Sorted!

We arrive back at our hotel by 4pm, in time for a short nap. That is one of the wonderful things about Old Fart tours. They cater for our slower pace and our need for regular nana naps, either at the hotel or on the bus if we are travelling during the day. And no one gets criticised on the bus for snoring, because most of us do anyway. Snore, that is.

We have an early dinner and then back onto the bus for an optional tour out to the pyramids again, this time for an evening Sound and Light Show. We don't know what to expect.

Upon entering an open space with many rows of cheap plastic chairs lined up, we are led to our group's allotted area and seated. The Sphinx and the three pyramids are in front of us. The seats around us fill up and the sun begins to dip in the sky. I realise it will soon be behind the pyramids. The evening is perfect. Balmy. Still. And then the magic happens.

It begins with the Sphinx lit eerily in a soft glow and an English voice emanating from it to narrate the evening's light show. I think it looks a bit cheesy to begin with, but then nature takes over and eclipses anything man might try to make of these great monuments.

The desert air is always dusty and, as the angle of the sun changes, the dust in the sky changes the light from glare to glow. Yellow at first, then gently to a soft orange and finally to a brilliant scarlet. As the sun drops behind the pyramids, they are silhouetted against these colours until they are black against the scarlet. It is breathtaking!

There is a laser light show going on down at the front of the crowd with sound effects, but I am transfixed by the natural light show happening before us. And on the horizon next to the pyramids we see the black silhouette of two camel-mounted policemen ambling slowly across the sand dunes. There are oohhs and aahhs all around us, as we are all affected by the timelessness of what we are witnessing. The sunset behind the pyramids has looked exactly like this for thousands of years. Again, I feel the link with those little men of the past working in the desert from sunrise to sunset. They would have seen the pyramids like this at sunset, but then they were new and in their full glory, clad in white polished limestone casing-stones that must have reflected the changing light like a mirror. It must have been an even more remarkable sight than it is now.

And then, as the sky finally darkens, the pyramids are lit up with a laser light show that is purely modern. The pyramids become glowing green, red, blue, gold and there are no words to describe how wonderful they look.

Suddenly, in the middle of this wonder, a pack of wild dogs wanders onto the scene. They seem to have come straight out of the desert and look like mangy dingos. Some of the ushers try to shoo them away, but they have come for the scraps that modern tourists always seem to leave in their wake. They are hungry and will not be deterred. Old chips packets, hamburger boxes, chocolate wrappers, any sort of snack that western tourists seem to drop as they go with the belief that "someone" will clean up after them is fair game for these dogs. There are about twenty of them in the pack, some of them only puppies. They start to wander in amongst the seated tourists. I see that they are thin, bony, starving and flea ridden. I wonder if rabies is a problem in Egypt and feel a little nervous.

A puppy runs along the row in front of me and a child, seeing how cute the puppy is, tosses a cold potato chip to it. Big mistake! Within seconds, a dozen starving dogs descend on the child and all hell breaks loose. The child's father scoops his progeny up out of harms way. The adults are standing and shooing the dogs away, the ushers are rushing through the rows of chairs with, of all things, brooms which they wave rather lamely at the dogs. Chairs are knocked over, women and children are screaming, men are swearing and kicking.

And suddenly, there is the inevitable policeman on his camel at the end of our row, his rifle slung over his shoulder. He raises his hand. I hold my breath. Oh gawd, is he going to shoot?

Nope. He blows a whistle instead. A dog whistle. High pitched, barely audible, but it sends the dogs crazy. They run along the rows of chairs and, within minutes, they have disappeared into the sand dunes from whence they came.

What fun! Hubby and I are laughing ourselves silly. This will make another great travel story to take home.

The mood on the bus back to the hotel is jovial. We wouldn't have missed this evening for anything.

As Hubby and I make our way to our room, we pass a smallish sign up on the corkboard where our daily itinerary is normally posted. The word "Alexandria" catches my attention and we stop to read it. Alexandria is not on the itinerary for this tour, but we read that there is a local tour available tomorrow.

Tomorrow is officially a rest day, but Hubby and I had agreed before we left for this trip that we would take whatever optional tours were available, because we would have all the time in the world to rest when we got back home. We have signed up for everything on offer, but this optional tour is being offered by a small local travel agency that has nothing to do with our tour company. It will leave at 6am and have us back to the hotel by 6pm. A full day, but then it is a three hour drive from Cairo to Alexandria and the tour covers a lot of ground once we get there. And of course there is the three hour drive back.

We decide to do it. We can book it from our room. As we walk away, I see an asterisk next to some very fine print at the bottom of the sign. Hubby's eyesight is better than mine, so I ask him to read it. Apparently, we each need to order a breakfast box for the morning, to be collected at reception before 6am, as there will be no stops on the way there or back. We get to our room, book the tour over the phone and order our breakfast boxes.

I hope there is a toilet on board the bus.

DAY 4

ALEXANDRIA

There isn't. A toilet. On the bus. In fact, it is a mini-bus seating only twelve people. There are six others besides us and we don't know any of them. We must have been the only members of our tour to see the sign, or perhaps the only ones who didn't need a rest day. The former, we guess, as quite a few of our tour are like us and don't want to miss anything. They would be here if they'd seen the sign.

We don't have a tour guide on the bus, just the driver. He speaks good English and hands us a tour sheet with roughly typed out details of the day ahead. Very amateur. I ask him if there will be a toilet stop on the way and he says politely that there won't be, as we need to get to Alexandria early in order to get all the sightseeing in. Goodness. That's

99

not good for Old Farts in the morning. We usually need to filter our morning coffee about an hour after breakfast. I decide not to drink any water until we have reached Alexandria. And to cross my legs.

Hubby puts our two breakfast boxes in the luggage shelf above us. We have had a quick look and they are quite impressive. Bottled water (Hubby has spares in his backpack), iced peach tea, bread rolls (Egyptian bread is sweet and soft and delicious eaten on its own), muffins, sweet and savoury biscuits, boiled eggs and fruit. Enough food for the whole day if necessary.

The seats are narrow, uncomfortable and the air conditioning is not working properly. We remind ourselves that this is how many people travel on less luxurious bus tours, and feel privileged to be able to afford our more upmarket tour company. But we acknowledge to ourselves that we are, quite frankly, simply too old for this sort of discomfort.

As we head off, we introduce ourselves to our travelling companions, male and female, aged between 30 and 50. We are the only Old Farts. Everyone is very friendly and we chat comfortably as the bus makes its way through the noisy traffic (even at this early hour) until we reach the road out of Cairo. From there, it is straight on through the desert.

We expected sand dunes all the way to Alexandria, but are very surprised to see miles and miles of new housing subdivisions. Not big enough to be suburbs, but rather enclaves. Each is made up of between ten to fifty ultra-modern homes within high gated walls. Most of the homes are unfinished, but where they have been finished, we see armed guards at the entry gates. Someone asks the driver about it, and he yells back to us that the Egyptian government is planning to relocate millions of Cairo citizens into these new areas, and then eventually demolish many of the slum areas of Cairo which will in turn be rebuilt. The armed guards are there to stop looters and homeless people from moving into the unfinished houses.

We are very impressed and ask the driver when it will be finished. He laughs and says that this will be completed in ten Egyptian years, one Egyptian year being the equivalent of about seven years in every other part of the world. That accounts for the vast majority of houses we see being unfinished. His implication is that it won't ever be completed.

Still, the intentions are very grand indeed.

An hour and a half into the drive, I begin to feel desperate for the loo. To distract me, Hubby takes one of the breakfast boxes down and we nibble away at the bread and muffins. The drinks can wait.

I notice no one else is eating their breakfast, but think nothing of it. It is, after all, only 7.30am and perhaps too early for some. Or maybe they ate before they left, which probably would have been wise.

We arrive in Alexandria at 9am, pull into a roadside service station and are told we have ten minutes. We nearly knock each other over to get to the loos. I only just make it. Gawd, that was close!

In Egypt, you pay to use the loos, usually one Egyptian pound, and you are given a single piece of toilet paper by the loo attendant. They don't seem to get the Western tourist's desire for more toilet paper. I mean, what do we do with it anyway? Which is why we travel with zip lock bags of tissues and wet wipes on us at all times. But here, we push past the attendants and hit those loos without a backward glance. Hubby hadn't enjoyed his morning ablute, so I know he'll be awhile, and when I have finished I pay the resentful attendant for me and for him, all the while watching the bus to make sure it doesn't leave without us. Come on, Hubby, push harder!

There is no time to get anything to eat. We are back on the bus and under way very quickly.

In a blur of speed, we are then taken to see a palace, a museum, a mosque, a Roman amphitheatre, another palace, the harbour, the city centre, some tombs, somebody's pillar, another mosque and a cemetery. My Point and Click camera is working overtime. We try to follow our route on our typed piece of paper, but give up in the end. We are off the bus, on the bus, off the bus, on the bus, off the bus, on the bus, and so on and so forth. We manage to find a toilet at one of the sights, but I don't remember which one. There were marble lions there and steps, but that's all I remember. And a last toilet stop at the last sight marked on the piece of paper before we get back on the bus.

And then it is 3pm, we are on the bus and heading back to Cairo. It is the worst optional tour we have ever experienced, badly planned and badly executed. All eight of us on the tour are hot, frazzled and a little more than pissed off. Not only were there no loo stops planned, there were no food stops either! Not even a half hour allowed for lunch somewhere. There was one cafe at one of the sights which sold icecreams in cones and we were tempted, but remembered the warnings regarding local dairy products and managed to resist.

This was not what we expected when we booked this tour. But then, we hadn't had time to research it as Hubby and I had done with all the other optional tours included with our normal tour. Trip Advisor is a great source of information and we heed the warnings, as well as the reassurances on that site. We wonder if this tinpot tour is even on Trip Advisor. It will be when Hubby has finished with it!

I am starving and very thirsty. We have cut back on our fluid intake because of the lack-of-a-loo situation, but decide it's time to get our breakfast boxes and finish them off. We hoe into the simple but abundant food and it tastes magnificent, as all food does when you are genuinely hungry.

As we eat, I am vaguely aware of an atmosphere building around us. I finish the bottle of now-tepid iced peach tea and look at our fellow travellers. They are glaring at us. Actually glaring with something akin to hatred.

And then the penny drops. We are the only ones with breakfast boxes! I poke Hubby and point this out to him. We turn to our six starving, dehydrated fellow travellers and ask them why they haven't got their breakfast boxes, too. They all have the same answer. They heard about this tour at the reception desk, booked it, but were not told about the breakfast boxes.

Oh gawd. We are the only ones with food, and our six comrades haven't eaten since the previous night. Poor buggers! Without hesitation, we hand over what is left. Hubby gets out the spare bottles of water from his backpack, we both take the muesli bars and gelatine lollies we always carry and share them around. We feel like saviours. We are treated like saviours! If only we'd realised earlier, we would happily have shared our food around.

By the time we get back to Cairo, we are all best friends, have exchanged email addresses and are laughing about the experience. But no one tips the bus driver as we get out. After all, he could have stopped for a quick loo break and a quick feed if he wanted to. It might have meant one less sight to see, but would we have even noticed? As it was, it was too much crammed into too little time.

It occurs to me then that our driver actually hasn't eaten or been to the loo himself during the whole day's drive. Maybe he ate big before he left home this morning, maybe he has a huge bladder. Maybe he had a pee up against a wall somewhere when we weren't looking. Or maybe he doesn't care and just wants to drive his little bus and collect his pay at the end of the week. Whatever the reason, before he has reached his own home, Hubby has the iPad out and is looking for some information on Trip Advisor about this tour. We find it, discover our experience is identical to everyone else's, and Hubby adds his own comment: "Don't do it!"

We shower, order room service for dinner and collapse on our bed. What a day! I'll have to go through the photos when we get home and try to figure out where I took them. Somewhere in Alexandria ...

DAY 5

ASWAN

The next morning, we have an obscenely early start. We set our own alarms for 3.00am, rise with some difficulty and are ready before the bedside phone rings with the official wake up call at 3.30am. We have been reassured that this will be the only very early call, and that it is necessary as we are to travel from Cairo to Aswan with a full day planned before joining our much anticipated cruise ship on the Nile. All we have time for is coffee and a pastry. No morning ablutions, I'm afraid. Which makes us feel a little nervous.

Even though I'm not quite awake, I take my pre-flight Valium. We have a short wait at the Cairo Airport, during which time I observe that most of our group are backwards and forwards to the

107

107

loo several times. I hope it's only the need for the morning ablute, and not the beginning of Cairo Tummy.

Our flight to Aswan takes us over the desert as the sun rises. We are low enough to see ripples on the sand dunes. Even though the air outside is still, there is a permanent mist of fine sand above the desert. It glows pink and orange in the morning light. Despite being inhospitable to human life, it is incredibly beautiful.

As we board our bus at the Aswan Airport, we can see our luggage being loaded into the bus's hold. Mohamed calls out to us. One of the suitcases has been damaged during the flight and the contents are spilling out. It is only held together by the strap secured tightly around it.

It is Hubby's suitcase. Damn! The zip appears to have broken. We examine the contents and believe nothing has been lost. Mohamed obtains a large plastic bag, fills it with the contents and loads it and the damaged suitcase carefully onto the bus. We'll sort it out when we get to the cruise ship on the Nile later that day.

We go to Lake Nasser to view the Aswan High Dam. At first, I think this might be rather boring. After all, I want to look at ancient monuments and temples, not some old dam. But what I find is one of the modern wonders of Egypt. We walk across the dam wall, listening to Mohamed tell us about the relocation of the Abu Simbel temple, the engineering accomplishments and the way the dam has changed the security of life on the Nile. And we understand that the clever people who built the pyramids are still clever people building dams to ensure that the Nile never dries up as it once used to. No water, no life. The ancient kingdoms of Egypt may have long gone, but modern Egypt is still impressive.

As we return to our bus, I see that Leslie has not left it. She is sitting at the front with her eyes closed, looking rather pale and clammy. I wonder if she has the dreaded Cairo Tummy.

Also on the bus is Mrs Teetering Heels. Mr Teetering Heels walked across the dam wall with the rest of us, but his missus obviously didn't think it was worth the effort in her pink and red high heeled mules. She is reading a book on her iPad and shows no interest in her husband's enthusiasm about the dam.

We then go on to a granite quarry where we see one of Queen Hatshepsut's obelisk's lying unfinished in the amongst the granite. A marvel of workmanship, even in its incomplete state. Leslie and Mrs Teetering Heels stay on the bus.

Then on to a small wharf where Mohamed herds us onto a motorboat, which will take us across the water to the Temple of Philae. Leslie remains on the bus again, looking decidedly seedy. Poor thing.

Mrs Teetering Heels, however, joins us for this excursion, but she nearly comes to grief getting on to the boat. One of her ridiculously high heels gets caught between the wharf and the boat and she almost tumbles headlong into the water. Her husband catches her just in time. She is quite shaken by the experience.

Mr Teetering Heels is also rattled, but for a different reason. He looked terrified as she headed towards the water and when he pulled her to safety, something inside the poor man snapped.

He helps her onto a seat on the boat and looks around. At the other end of the wharf are several market stalls with the usual cheap tourist tat on offer. Mr Teetering Heels sets his jaw with determination and pushes his way past the rest of us still getting on the boat, then strides across the wharf to the market stalls. A minute later, he boards the boat again with something in his hand. He thrusts it at his wife.

Mrs Teetering Heels looks with horror at the poorly made leather sandals he is holding out to her. They are ... flat! She shakes her head and opens her mouth to protest, but before she can make a sound, he is down on one knee, whipping off her clattery sandals and slipping on the flat sandals.

She is rendered speechless. And so are the rest of us. We hope we are not about to witness a marital dispute.

Mr Teetering Heels stands with the gaudy high heeled sandals in his hand and looks down at her. There is no anger in his face, only love and concern. She reaches up for the sandals and he makes as if to throw them overboard.

I want to laugh. This is wonderful. Anything out of the ordinary is grist for a writer's mill and this is certainly out of the ordinary. I don't believe Mr and Mrs Teetering Heels have ever had a face-off quite like this. They both look a little confused by it, but he is determined to win. He says, "You can have them back when we are on the bus."

She squeaks, "But I want them now!"

"You almost fell into the water."

"But I didn't, did I? You stopped me."

"I'm always stopping you. From falling. I've been stopping you for seventeen years."

"I know. You are such a dear. But you know I can't wear flat shoes."

"Why not? Everyone else does."

"Because ..." Mrs Teetering Heels looks around at all of us crammed onto this very small boat. We are pretending not to hear by looking out over the water or down at our laps or anywhere but at the duelling couple, but every one of us is listening intently. She lowers her voice to a whisper, but as we are all within a metre or two of her, we hear every word. " ...because flat shoes make me look short and fat!"

Hubby slaps his hand over my mouth before I can burst out laughing. Mrs Teetering Heels could be wearing six foot high shoes and she'd still look short and fat because ... well, she is short and fat!

Ms Fat 'n Loud, the marvellous outspoken career nurse that she is, looks up to address Mrs Teetering Heels directly. "I'd rather be short and fat than drowned at the bottom of Lake Nasser or laid up in hospital with a broken hip and a cracked skull!"

Mrs Teetering Heels looks at Ms Fat 'n Loud. Really looks at her. She sees not a short and fat woman, but a tall and fat woman who is fine about being tall and fat. She sees an unattractive woman who is completely comfortable in her own stretched and saggy skin. And she sees someone who's personality is so forceful that it doesn't do to argue with her.

"I suppose so," she mumbles. She looks down at the tatty sandals on her feet. "But they aren't very nice, are they?"

Shopping Sister 2 pipes up. "There'll be some nicer ones at some of the other markets. We've already bought some."

Shopping Sister 1 adds her bit. "I've got a red pair, all leather with coloured glass beading on them."

Shopping Sister 3 says, "I've got blue ones with silver sequins. So many to choose from. We'll help you get some nice ones."

Mrs Teetering Heels looks around her rather pathetically. We all give her encouraging smiles. After all, we are a family after yesterday's events and we'll look out for each other now. "Alright. But they hurt my feet ..."

Miss Know-it-all states, "That's because the Achilles tendons at the back of your heels have shortened from wearing high heels for so long. They'll hurt for a day or two, but if you do some stretches, they'll settle down."

Mrs Teetering Heels looks to Ms Fat 'n Loud for confirmation, who concurs with Miss Know-it-all with the usual exclamations. "I expect your feet are practically deformed from those high heels! Not to mention the strain on your knees, hips and back! A few simple stretches will do you good! I'll show you what to do, don't worry! You'll start to feel a lot better in a few days!"

Mr Teetering Heels sighs heavily, puts the dangerous sandals in his backpack and settles down next to his wife. He puts his arm around her comfortingly. This is a life changing experience for her and he understands it will take time to process.

Hubby takes his hand away from my mouth. It's safe to do so now.

The Temple of Philae is, like everything in Egypt, a magnificent experience. We stroll through the tall columns and marvel that the temple was completely dismantled in the 1960's and relocated to a higher island to protect it from the rising waters of the Aswan Dam. Mr Twinkling Eyes says, "Looks like another pile of rocks to me." His wife grins at him.

We listen to Mohamed tell us about the history of Philae and then pass around his iPad with the painting of the Temple done in 1800, showing its original colours before repeated flooding washed them away. Breathtaking.

Hubby and I then find ourselves seeking shade with Mr and Mrs Twinkling Eyes and Mr and Mrs Gentle Wit as we all sit on some large blocks of stone and swig from our bottles of water. The heat is wearying.

Mrs Twinkling Eyes says, "We can tick this one off our bucket list now."

I say, "You have a bucket list, too?"

We then discuss our bucket lists. At our age, we have a sense of time running out and we all have goals to reach while our health holds out. As we talk, Mr and Mrs Red Pants stroll past us with Mohamed. I hear Mr Red Pants, who is thankfully lucid today, tell Mohamed that, with his education, he could be a professor at just about any university in the world. Then Mohamed tells him that he once considered doing that, but then mentions how much he earns as a tour guide in Egypt. Mr and Mrs Red Pants look at each other in shock. Mr Red Pants tells Mohamed that tour guides here earn more than twice what he earned in Boston as a history professor at a prestigious university. Mrs Red Pants jokes that maybe it is time her husband changed jobs. They share a laugh.

The irony of this conversation is not lost on us who have accidentally eavesdropped. There is no future for Mr Red Pants. Their bucket list will end with this trip. I comment on how fortunate we six are and we agree. It is hot, we are tired, but we have nothing to complain about. Nothing at all.

One should always know when one is well off.

The time comes for us to make our way back to the boat. We six walk together. Mohamed and Mr and Mrs Red Pants are ahead of us. We see Mr and Mrs Socially Superior walking with Mr and Mrs Intelligentsia, the two men having a conversation about which Margaret River red they prefer. They don't appear to be in complete accord. Mrs Intelligentsia is going on about something to do with the Philae Temple history. Mrs Socially Superior is not listening. She is beetroot red (she will not wear a hat because it will flatten her teased hair), the sweat pours off her and she is intent on getting back to the shade of the boat.

Mr and Mrs Effusive are walking with Mr and Mrs Teetering Heels. Mrs Effusive is sympathising with Mrs Teetering Heel's complaints about how sore her feet and ankles are in these awful flat sandals. Mrs Effusive jollies her along by telling her that at least she is safe in flats. Mr Effusive and Mr Teetering Heels, both being laconic in nature, walk behind their wives in companionable silence.

Mr and Mr Gay Couple are walking with the 3 Shopping Sisters. Mr Gay Man 2 is foraging around inside the Sisters' shopping bags, checking out their market stall purchases. Every tourist site in Egypt has market stalls and the Shopping Sisters will explore them all. We hear Mr Gay Man 1, the tall elegant half of this love match, tell the Sisters that they would love New York, as the shopping there is simply fabulous. They are quite excited by this revelation. Mr Gay Man 2 tells them they can stay with them if they visit, as they have a large apartment with guest accommodation and wouldn't it be fun!

The 2 Texan Gals are walking with Ms Fat 'n Loud and Miss Know-it-all. Texas Gal 1 and Miss Know-it-all are exchanging useless trivia in fierce competition. Ms Fat 'n Loud is expounding her theories on ancient Egyptian birth rituals. Texas Gal 2 is nodding politely, but basically ignoring all three of them.

Ms Miseryguts is walking with Mrs Love-a-chat. No one wants to talk to Ms Miseryguts and no one wants to listen to Mrs Love-a-chat. They are a perfect match for each other.

Leslie is walking between the Two Oldies, her arms linked with theirs as they make their way carefully over the uneven ground, the two walking sticks tap tapping away.

Miss Well Travelled is happily strolling along on her own, looking around her with the pleasure of a chocoholic in a chocolate factory. Just being here is all she needs.

So the factions have begun. Factions always develop on these bus tours. We've seen it over and over. It's human nature to seek out your own kind, or the opposite to yourself as a balance to your own foibles. It usually takes a few weeks, but perhaps the events of the last few days have hastened it. We seem to have learned more about each other in a shorter time than usual. Crisis will do that.

The factions seem oblivious that they are now factions. It has occurred naturally, without conflict, and in my humble opinion, will work for the duration of this rather long tour. I like our own little group of six. I am content.

We climb on board the boat and find two Nubians selling their jewellery. We woman gravitate to them straight away. The men roll their eyes, sigh and take their seats. I come away with two necklaces and several bangles. By the time we reach shore and board our bus, the Nubians have sold just about everything. They have done well out of our relatively small group.

The bus takes us to another wharf, where we are transferred to several feluccas, the traditional small sailing vessels of the Egyptian Nile. I hadn't thought this would be much of an experience, but I am wrong.

As we leave the shore and sail around an island, a silence descends on us. I can't remember exactly who was on board with us (we were divided onto three feluccas) because I am overcome with a sense of how timeless this relatively small boat is. This is exactly how the ancients traversed the Nile, with only the wind in the sail and the water gently lapping against the side of the small vessel. It is soothing and amazingly cool on the water. For half an hour, no one speaks. We are all affected by the meditative mood.

Then we are back onto the wharf with, "Oh no! More steps!" behind us and onto our airconditioned bus. A short trip later and we arrive at the banks of the Nile where we see our cruise ship.

118

Mohamed had warned us not to call it a boat. It is a ship bearing the name of one of my favourite opera characters. Long, two storied, very modern looking, a great first impression. We file on board and there are oohs and aahs from everyone. The reception area is plush and luxurious. It is a floating five star hotel.

Half a dozen young Egyptian lads in spotless white tunics and black trousers are lined up, waiting to assist us. Our bags have already been delivered to our rooms and, as soon as we are given our room numbers, we make our way there.

Hubby and I are not disappointed. Our room is large, the bed enormous, the bathroom beautifully appointed and glass sliding doors lead to our own private balcony overlooking the Nile. And it is airconditioned and marvellously cool.

The only fly in the ointment is the large plastic bag of Hubby's suitcase contents and the dead suitcase sitting next to it.

Death Of A Suitcase On The Nile. Not quite Hercule Poirot territory, but a problem nevertheless.

On cue, there is a knock at our door and Mohamed comes in to inspect the suitcase. He asks us if we want it repaired or would prefer a new piece of luggage. The zip looks damaged beyond repair to us, and the suitcase has been around the world several times, so we opt for a new piece of luggage.

Mohamed tells us there is a department store in Aswan with a good selection of luggage. He has bought several items from that store himself. He will arrange for us to be taken by taxi to the store. Our ship doesn't sail for at least another couple of hours, so we have plenty of time. He leaves to speak to one of the boat boys about it.

A few minutes later, there is another knock at the door. A youth of about 17 tells us his name is Ahmed and he will take us to the taxi. He is a charming young man, immaculately dressed and immaculately mannered.

Ahmed escorts me and Hubby out of the ship onto the wharf where there is a line of taxis waiting for business. We expect him to take us to the first taxi in the line, but instead he heads for a taxi about halfway along the rank. We follow him obediently. After all, he must know what he is doing. He is greeted warmly by a skinny man not much older than him. They shake hands and pat each other's backs. As their hands separate, I see that money has been exchanged. The taxi driver has slipped a couple of notes to Ahmed. I'm not sure what that means. The two young men have a brief discussion in Arabic and Ahmed returns to the ship.

The taxi driver opens the back door and indicates that we should get in. As we do so, the taxi drivers who had been waiting ahead of him in the line start to gather around. There appears to be a heated exchange going on. Our taxi driver pulls away quickly, leaving a half dozen men shaking fists at him.

I feel a little nervous. But I trust Mohamed, so I'm sure we are alright. Mohamed wouldn't send us into any danger.

We are zooming along the road into town. Not as busy as Cairo, but full of beeping and honking horns as the taxi weaves it's way between the other cars.

Hubby leans forward and says, "Do you speak English?"

The driver answers us with, "Yes, sir, I speak very good English."

"Good. Can you take us to the department store to buy a suitcase?"

"Yes, sir, I will take you to buy a new suitcase. The best suitcase in Aswan for you, sir."

OK.

The driver takes a mobile phone from his pocket and, one hand on the wheel, makes a call, speaking in a rapid, high voice to someone. He ends the call and pockets the phone again.

Why do I feel even more nervous?

We drive towards Aswan, passing between some quite modern buildings. We can see what appears to be a shopping centre up ahead. Suddenly, the taxi turns off into a side road, travels a hundred metres and turns again into a narrow alley flanked by shop fronts. Small, old and rather shabby looking shopfronts. Goods are displayed on the sidewalk. Everything from clothing to electrical goods, kitchen utensils and computers. Locals are out in force, browsing and shopping. It is a very busy alleyway.

But it doesn't look like a department store.

Hubby leans forward again and says, "Is this the way to the department store?"

"Yes, sir. You buy very good suitcase."

I'm feeling butterflies in my stomach and Hubby is frowning a little. We have no choice but to keep going. After all, we have no idea where we are, except that we are somewhere in Aswan in Egypt. We can trust the taxi driver. Can't we?

My heart is beating a little faster.

The taxi stops in front of what looks like a souvenir shop. There are trinkets, scarves, clothing, leather goods, tourist souvenirs and various other things on display on the sidewalk. A wizened old man wearing a baggy brown galabeya approaches the taxi, opens the back door and greets us with a huge, toothless smile. "Welcome, sir and madam. We have very nice suitcase for you."

This is not a department store. We smell a rat.

Hubby says to the taxi driver, "We were told that we would be taken to a department store."

The driver says sweetly, "Good bargain here for you sir. Just for you."

The old man says, "Just for you, sir and madam. Very good bargain."

Oh gawd.

Hubby and I exchange glances. We are genuinely anxious.

The driver says, "I will wait here for you, sir. Very good bargain just for you!"

He will wait for us. That means a safe trip back to the ship. After we have done our shopping. For some reason, I feel reassured.

The old man is indicating his shop with a sweeping hand and that huge grin. Hubby says, "Come on, we'll have a look. If it isn't what we want, we'll ask to be taken to the department store."

"Alright."

We get out of the taxi.

The old man smells of stale cigarette smoke and spices. He shuffles towards the back of the shop and points at two stools. "Please to sit?" We do as we are told.

Another man, middle-aged, but just as toothless, comes out of the back of the shop and smiles at us. "Sir and madam would like some tea?"

I shake my head. I'm not game.

"Very nice tea, sir and madam."

Hubby says, "We'd just like to buy a suitcase."

The old man says, "Yes, yes, sir, but you have very nice tea first."

Hubby looks at me. He sees my wide, imploring eyes. "No tea. We just want to see some suitcases."

"Yes, yes, we have many fine suitcases." The old man goes into the back room and comes back with two large, cheap suitcases.

The middle-aged man produces a small table and puts it in front of us. He then goes into the back room and returns with - you guessed it - tea! I whisper to Hubby, "Don't you dare! We don't know where the water came from!"

But the middle-aged man is pouring two small glasses of hot tea and hands one to Hubby. He is most insistent. Hubby looks into the face of this man and decides not to argue with him. He takes the tea and sips it. I refuse my tea and rub my tummy, pulling a face. The man says, "Oh, I am sorry, madam. Many fine tourists such as yourself get the stomach pains in Egypt. I have medicine for that ..."

"No!" I say, rather too sharply. The man smiles his obsequious smile and backs away. I hope I haven't offended him. "No, thank you. I have medicine for it already."

"Yes, madam."

The old man puts the two suitcases in front of us. They are cheap plastic affairs, knock-offs with good brand names which don't fool us at all.

"Very nice suitcases for you, sir and madam. Very good bargain."

Hubby looks at me. "What do you think?"

"I think that if we don't get back to the ship soon, we might literally miss the boat."

"Yes. We could take one of these for now and get something better when we get back to Cairo. We have a free day there."

I am anxious to get out of here. My over active imagination already has a sedative in the tea my husband just sipped. And what will happen to me when he passes out? Ridiculous, I know, but I don't feel safe. "Alright."

Hubby takes another sip of tea, points to the larger of the two suitcases and addresses the old man. "How much?"

"Very good bargain for you. Only 400 Egyptian pounds."

Hubby nearly chokes on his tea. I want to laugh.

"How much for the other one?"

"Also very good bargain. Also 400 Egyptian pounds."

Hubby looks at me incredulously, then I see "that look" in his eyes. Once a Scotsman, always a

Scotsman. He's going to get the better of this little man. He's going to do a deal.

The bargaining begins. Backwards and forwards until Hubby has it down to 50 Egyptian pounds and the little old man is almost weeping because his family will starve and he will go out of business and Hubby is too hard on him. But I see a gleam of victory in the old man's eyes as we hand over the 50 pounds and take our purchase out to the waiting taxi.

The middle-aged man rushes to open the taxi door for us. As we take our seats with the suitcase sitting between us, I see the man lean in through the driver's window and shake hands. With the inevitable notes exchanged.

We know we have been rorted, but what can we do about it?

The driver takes us back to the wharf and pulls up at the end of the line of waiting taxis. No sooner has he stopped than our taxi is surrounded by all the other drivers. They begin yelling at our young driver in Arabic, then a few start pounding on the bonnet of the already dented taxi and screaming at him through the window. The young man seems unfazed, but I am really scared. I try to open the door to get out and discover to my horror that there are no handles on the inside of the back doors. We are at the mercy of the taxi driver.

Hubby leans forward and commands, "Let us out!"

The driver looks at my frightened face and leaps out. He opens my door and I exit very fast. The other drivers are still yelling at him, but he seems immune to them.

Hubby follows me out and, with suitcase in hand, we make our way quickly back to the ship. The screaming match continues behind us.

It is only when we get to the safety of the reception area that we realise we haven't paid the taxi driver. Hubby says he should go back to pay him, but I tell him we should speak to Mohamed first. We really aren't quite sure what just happened.

Reception phones through to Mohamed and he is with us in moments. He listens to our story with growing anger. "This is very bad," he says. "This should not have happened." He looks at the new suitcase. "Are you happy with the suitcase?"

Hubby looks down at it and says, "It's a piece of rubbish, but it might do until we get to Cairo. We should be able to get something better there."

"How much did you pay for it?"

"50 Egyptian pounds."

"Oh, no. It is only worth 5."

The Scotsman does not want to hear that. Someone got the better of him!

Mohamed makes a decision. He takes the suitcase and says, "I will look after this matter for you. I am very sorry. I trusted Ahmed, but he has done wrong."

We aren't sure what he means, but we give him the suitcase. He tells us he will contact us as soon as he has sorted things out.

Back in our room, we are still confronted with the damaged suitcase and the plastic bag of contents. We flop onto the bed to recover for a few moments. Then there is a knock at the door.

Mohamed is standing there with Ahmed. A very chastened Ahmed who hangs his head in shame as Mohamed speaks. "Ahmed will apologise. It was his cousin in the taxi. His cousin gave him money to use his taxi. The other taxi drivers were angry because he jumped the queue. He then took you to the shop of his father and grandfather, who are also the uncle and grandfather of Ahmed. When you came back, the other drivers were waiting for him. Ahmed's cousin will not be welcome at this particular taxi rank again. This is not the way we treat tourists in Egypt. Ahmed will pay back the bribe to his cousin and return the suitcase to his uncle and grandfather who will refund you. And Ahmed will pay for the repair of your old suitcase out of his own pay."

We are stunned.

Ahmed, almost in tears and visibly trembling under the wrath of Mohamed, says, "I am sorry, sir and madam. I will take the damaged suitcase to my mother at once."

We hand over the damaged suitcase to Ahmed. Mohamed snaps an instruction to Ahmed in Arabic. The youth hurries off. Mohamed says, "Ahmed's mother is a seamstress. She will repair the zip at no expense to you. It will be returned to you within the hour. I am very embarrassed and sorry that you have been through this terrible experience."

Hubby and I look at each other. This will make a great travel story!

I say, "What will happen to Ahmed?"

"He will be dismissed. We do not take things like this lightly."

I am sorry to hear this. "How long has he been working here?"

"This is his first week."

I give Hubby a meaningful look, then say, "He's very young. Everyone makes mistakes when they are young. Can you give him a second chance?"

"If that is your wish, then he can be placed on a warning instead of being dismissed."

"Please. I'm sure he's frightened enough not to do anything like that again."

Mohamed smiles at us. "Perhaps you are right. I was young once myself. I will let him know that this is your request."

"Thank you."

Mohamed leaves and we lay down on the bed again. We are exhausted.

After a short nap, we shower and change. There is a knock at the door. Ahmed is there with the damaged suitcase in hand, and our money returned. He sheepishly shows Hubby that the zip has indeed been repaired. In fact, a new zip has been sewn in with several rows of stitching to secure it in place. It will do until we get back to Cairo. Then he thanks us for not having him dismissed and says that he will be the best boat boy on ship from now on. He means it, too. A job is a job in any country in the world.

We thank Ahmed for his apology, wish him well and close the door on that episode.

It is time for dinner. We decide to explore the boat before we eat.

The dining room is silver service, the bar is open 24 hours, there is a large room with comfortable sofas scattered around under the chandeliers, and the ever present boat boys are waiting to meet our every need. Including Ahmed, who smiles nervously at us.

We continue to wander around the ship. Everything is polished, gleaming and beautiful. And every window looks out onto the Nile and its riverbanks.

We see a sign for the pool and outdoor bar pointing to some stairs, climb them and find ourselves in a dream world. The top of the ship is one long pool and bar area. Banana lounges are spread out around the bar with large canvas sails providing much needed shade. It is hot and humid up here, but as I love the heat and humidity, it is perfect for me. We get ourselves a cold drink and find a couple of seats. We are soon joined by Mr and Mrs Twinkling Eyes and Mr and Mrs Gentle Wit.

There are a number of strangers sitting around the pool, most of them in bathing suits. It's not an attractive sight. They are all Old Farts, like us, and the display of stretch marks, spider veins, wrinkly skin and fat is what you would expect at our age. But they couldn't care less. And neither do we, because we all look the same under our clothes. So, good for them!

We learn from one of the barmen that we are sharing the ship with another tour group of British tourists. They have their rooms at one end of the ship, we at the other end. But we will share the common spaces with them. One of them, a pasty, pudgy, wobbly woman in a black bathing suit, comes to the bar for a drink. We hail her and engage her in conversation. She tells us that her group are all part of a travel club in England, they all know each other, and that they do a Nile cruise every year. Normally, they do it in the northern hemisphere winter, but Britain is suffering a very cold wet spring this year, so they have booked an extra cruise, with most of the club here around the pool.

I look around me at this magical place and understand why. If it wasn't such a long, long way from Australia, we might do the same. But if we want a short escape, we can content ourselves with a couple of weeks in Cairns or Port Douglas to get away from the cold Canberra winter. We enjoy those locations, but they will never look the same after this.

The sun lowers in the sky and the light is incredible. Most of our group are on the upper deck with us now. I look around and feel as if David Suchet will appear any minute now as Hercule Poirot to solve the Murder On The Nile.

The dinner gong is sounded and we go downstairs.

DAY 6

ABU SIMBEL

The following morning offers a choice - relax on the ship or take an optional excursion to Abu Simbel. Our entire group chooses the excursion, even Miss Well Travelled who tells us it is her fifth visit. We observe that the British group all stay on the boat. They've done all the temples and monuments, they are here for the warmth, the luxury and the pampering. They aren't going anywhere.

Did I use the word warmth?

As we Old Farts walk off the airconditioned ship, we are hit with a heat that nearly knocks even heating-seeking me off my feet. We clamber aboard the bus and spend a short time in the cool before being offloaded at a small airport where we are to board a plane for a half hour flight to the

Abu Simbel site. I have taken my pre-flight Valium, despite the flight being so short. Flying is flying to someone who suffers from flying anxiety.

We have done our research on Abu Simbel. We know that two magnificent temples were carved into the side of a mountain and threatened with submersion when the Aswan Dam was built and Lake Nasser created. A great international collaboration was begun and the temples were carefully dismantled, moved to higher ground and rebuilt. An extraordinary feat and one of the great highlights for me and Hubby on this trip. We board the plane in great excitement, trying to ignore the incredible heat and the gritty wind. And the fact that the plane looks like a reject from the Second World War. It is old. Like us. An Old Fart plane.

We discover the air conditioning on the plane doesn't work. For half an hour, we are mainly concerned with finding enough air to keep us breathing until we land and they let us out. It distracts us from the bumpy ride. The wind seems to increase as we cross the desert. I look down at the sea of sand and again, marvel that the Egyptians have survived here for so long.

Most of us have headaches by the time we board another bus to take us to the temple site. And this bus doesn't have air conditioning either. At least you can open the windows, but that just lets the fierce hot air in.

As we pull into the Abu Simbel car park, we see that we are very definitely not alone. Hundreds of people are alighting from dozens of buses around us. Mohamed raises a stick with a red scarf on it and we follow the red scarf through the throng of fellow tourists.

We pass through an open cafeteria area with wonky plastic chairs and equally wonky plastic tables. No cooling here, even under the covered patio. I look up to see that the covering was once some sort of brush, but the wind has dislodged most of it so that there is more sun than shade.

Mohamed informs us that we will need to walk down a rough track to the temples, that we have an hour to wander around inside the temples, and then we need to follow the track around the other side of the temples and back up here to the cafeteria. He warns us to keep up our fluids and wear our hats. Then he tells us that it is actually 50 degrees centigrade in the shade today.

Gawd help us! If it is that hot in the shade, what will it be when we leave the shade to walk down to the temple? I'm glad I have my insulated parasol with me.

Leslie asks the Two Oldies if they really want to do this. They both nod. It's too hot for them to speak, but they don't want to miss this experience. They are wearing good, wide brimmed cloth hats and have water bottles in their bags. Leslie takes each of them by the arm and walks between them as they carefully pick their way over the track with their walking sticks. I think Leslie was hoping the Two Oldies wouldn't want to walk to the temple in this heat, as she is looking a little washed out herself. They would have been a legitimate excuse to sit in the hot cafeteria and wait for the rest of us. But she does her duty. She's a good sort.

I put up my parasol and Hubby and I make our way down the track. I can hardly breath, it is so hot, and I can feel the wind cutting across my face like sandpaper.

We see that our group are mostly sensibly dressed with light clothes and hats, even Mrs Teetering Heels who is wearing her cheap flat sandals, which are clearly hurting her as she groans with every step. At least she has less chance of falling. The exception is Mrs Socially Superior who is wearing the predictable ballet flats, black polyester trousers and a white polyester top - but no hat. She will not crush that teased hair, no matter what! I'm having trouble breathing in this fierce hot wind, so I can't imagine how she is feeling inside all that polyester and thick makeup.

We all make it to the temples. The discomfort is worth it, for they are truly magnificent. Mohamed points out various things of interest inside the temples, including one figure sporting a large erect penis etched into a pillar. The penis itself is blackened and worn, and Mohamed tells us that there is a legend that barren women will bear children if they rub the carved penis. Thousands of years of rubbing has worn and stained it.

Now, we female Old Farts are way past our child bearing years, but we can't resist giving that erection a good old rub and sharing a giggle as we do so. The exception is, of course, Ms Miseryguts, whose sour face becomes even sourer (is that even a word?) as she turns away with disgust. Old Oldie, on the other hand, rubs it the hardest and says, "That's the closest I'll ever get to one of those again," and we girls laugh. Our husbands pretend not to notice.

We leave the shade of the temples and begin the walk back to the cafeteria. It is uphill and lined with sparsely planted trees which cast a little shade across the track every few metres. Every bit of our energy is put into traversing that uphill track. Hubby and I hold the parasol close to our heads and dash from patch of shade to patch of shade. Whereas the track down to the temples was quite rough and rocky, the track back up is paved and

137

stepped. We ignore the repeated, "Oh no! More steps!" in the Texan accent behind us. We ignore the wheezing of Ms Fat 'n Loud as we pass her. We ignore Leslie and the Two Oldies who are getting slower and slower in front of us. We ignore Mrs Love-a-Chat who is rambling on about how good she is at going up hills, but that this is a bit too much. And we just plain ignore Ms Miseryguts. I know she's moaning about something, but who cares? It's every man/woman for themselves until we reach the respite of the cafeteria.

This feels like the hardest thing I have ever done, and I've done four childbirths, so that is saying something! We finally reach the cafeteria and collapse into a couple of chairs, swigging from our water bottles until they are empty. Hubby goes to find more drinks and returns with warm iced tea and water. The fridges are out of order! I don't complain, it's wet and we down it gratefully. He asks if I need more and I nod gratefully. He goes back to get them.

Most of our group is with us now, even the laggers who are standing around limply, looking for chairs to sit in. As the men make their way towards the cafeteria counter to get drinks for their women, bless them, the vacated chairs are quickly taken.

And then two things happen in quick succession. Two things that take us all completely by surprise.

First, I'm aware of Mrs Socially Superior arriving to stand next to me. Her husband has gone with most of the men to get more drinks. She is breathing noisily and with some difficulty, and her clothes are saturated with sweat. It's actually running down her legs and forming pools around her shoes. I look around for a chair for her, then see something red out of the corner of my eye. I turn to look and, with horror, see that Mrs Socially Superior is bleeding from every finger. I look up at her and am astonished to find her face is sliding down onto her chest. Am I hallucinating?

Then as I find the sweet spot in my multifocals, I realise that Mrs Socially Superior is not bleeding. She is wearing false red fingernails and the heat has melted the glue so that they are now hanging by gluey threads from her weakly dangling fingers. As for her face - her makeup has been separated from her face by the copious sweating and literally slipped down her neck to settle on her chest. The pancake makeup, the eyeshadow, the false eyelashes, the pencilled eyebrows, the blusher and lipstick - there they all are, sitting just above her cleavage in a grotesque mask. What is left behind is a badly sunburnt, red, freckled, sweating bare face with small eyes and no eyebrows. She doesn't look well at all!

I rise to offer her my seat just as Mrs Twinkling Eyes and Mrs Gentle Wit come up behind her. And then something changes. I'm not sure what it is at first, then I realise that I can't hear Mrs Socially Superior breathing. Oh gawd, something is seriously wrong here!

Then Mrs Socially Superior's eyes roll backwards and she begins to sag to the ground. I call out, "She's going!", grab her by the arms and Mrs Twinkling Eyes and Mrs Gentle Wit grab her from behind to ensure a soft landing. As she hits the ground, she starts breathing again, but it is barely breathing, more like gasping.

Within seconds, the women in our group are gathering around the unconscious woman and we become a family again, rushing to the aid of one of our own. I hear heavy wheezing approach and Ms Fat 'n Loud lowers herself with some difficulty to join me, Mrs Twinkling Eyes and Mrs Gentle Wit on our knees. I see a flash of white cotton and Mohamed is standing by me. I look for Leslie and see her coming towards us in a great hurry, followed more slowly by the Two Oldies. Most of the men are just realising that something has happened and are making their way towards us.

And then the second thing happens.

The group parts to allow Leslie in. And Leslie collapses. Just like that! She starts by sagging at the knees, sits on her backside, rolls onto her side and she's out cold. Right next to Mrs Socially Superior. The two of them laid out together side by side with Ms Fat 'n Loud between them.

I hear Ms Miseryguts' whining voice above me. "They're dead! They're both dead!"

Miss Know-it-all snaps, "No, they're not! Probably just fainted with the heat."

Mrs Love-a-Chat says, "I remember one time when I fainted ..." and we all tune out.

Miss Well Travelled kneels next to us and says to Ms Fat 'n Loud, "You're a nurse, aren't you? Are they alright?"

Ms Fat 'n Loud is already on the job. She checks for a pulse on each woman, makes a satisfied "hhmm" sound, which we assume to mean that both are alive, then proceeds to give her patients a quick examination, pinching skin and lifting eyelids. Then she slaps Mrs Socially Superior across the face, hard. We all flinch. She calls out, "Wake up! Come on, wake up!" There is no response.

She then does the same to Leslie. We all flinch again. Leslie gives a sigh and opens her eyes. And then she does something that every mother and grandmother in our group instantly recognises.

141

She brings both her hands up and crosses them protectively over her small round stomach.

OK.

I exchange a knowing glance with Mrs Twinkling Eyes and Mrs Gentle Wit.

Ms Fat 'n Loud leans down and says bluntly, "How many weeks?"

Leslie takes a minute to focus, then looks up at our understanding and sympathetic faces. "Sixteen. Am I alright?"

"Have you had any problems?"

"No."

"A recent ultrasound?"

"Last week. Everything was fine." Leslie is looking frightened.

Ms Fat 'n Loud pats her hand and says gently (which surprises all of us), "You know I'm a midwife, don't you? Good. I expect you are dehydrated and you've had a drop in blood pressure, which caused you to faint. It's quite common, especially in these conditions. Do you mind if I check out your tummy?"

"What about..."

"Her pulse is good and she's breathing. Heat stroke, I suspect. I just want to be sure you're not contracting. It will only take a minute."

Leslie nods gratefully. She senses she is in good hands. And so do we.

Mrs Socially Superior continues to breath in short gasps. I figure that as long as we can hear that, she's alright.

Without instruction, our group form a wall of privacy around us. I'm aware of it, even though my attention is still on Mrs Socially Superior and Leslie. Something frightening is happening to Mrs Socially Superior and something deeply personal is happening to Leslie, and our newfound family is keeping the strangers away.

And haven't they gathered quickly! As the strangers form a crowd around us, our women form a tight circle, their concerned faces looking down at us. Our men, oddly enough, turn their backs on us to face the growing crowd and politely resist the pressure of curious onlookers. There is female stuff going on at their feet and they pay Leslie their respect by not looking.

Ms Fat 'n Loud gently palpates Leslie's abdomen. "Any pain?" Leslie shakes her head. She is wearing a blue cotton dress and without warning, Ms Fat 'n Loud swiftly lifts the hem of the dress and looks underneath. She gives Leslie a satisfied nod. She is not having a miscarriage. "You are probably alright, but I want you checked over by a doctor."

She quickly turns back to the still unconscious Mrs Socially Superior, who is, thankfully, still breathing in strange shallow gasps, then looks around for Mr Socially Superior. He is standing next to Hubby, who has his back turned to us along with the other men, but he holds drinks in his hands and is looking down at his wife with some confusion. Ms Fat 'n Loud wastes no time with niceties. "Does your wife have any pre-existing medical conditions?"

He shakes his head. "I don't think so."

"What do you mean, you don't think so?"

"I ... well ..."

"Come on, man, you should know!"

"She's usually alright. She's a bit of a drama queen ..."

"Well, she's not being a drama queen now! Does she have a heart condition? Hypertension? Diabetes? Is she taking any medication?"

"No, not that I know of."

Ms Fat 'n Loud is disgusted. As are we all. If it was me down here on the ground, Hubby would already be on his knees by my side and could list my drugs and medical issues without any problems, as I could his.

Ms Fat 'n Loud grabs hold of Mohamed's galabeya and pulls him down on his knees. She says quickly, "This woman is probably suffering from heat stroke, but I can't diagnose her properly here. She needs IV fluids urgently and blood tests done to rule out a cardiac event or any other underlying condition. Her condition is currently serious and if we don't get her to a hospital quickly, we could lose her. I want an ambulance for her and for Leslie and I want it NOW!"

"Yes, yes of course," Mohamed says, and he swings into action. He rises, strides away and gets busy on his mobile phone.

Everyone is frightened. We all heard the words "serious" and "lose her".

A very large crowd has gathered around us now. I hear many different languages discussing the situation. The heat is suffocating.

I am still on my knees with Mrs Twinkling Eyes and Mrs Gentle Wit. Ms Fat 'n Loud says to us, "Help Leslie up slowly and sit her in a chair. Give her water and something salty, potato crisps or whatever you can find. If she faints again, put her head between her knees. Got that?"

We nod and do as we are told, getting Leslie to her feet and sitting her in the nearest chair. Miss Well Travelled stays with Ms Fat 'n Loud. I hear her say she has first aid training and would like to help if she can. Ms Fat 'n Loud nods her acknowledgement and the two women hover over Mrs Socially Superior.

Mohamed returns and begins to move the crowd back with the help of the other tour guides. There is no resistance. Everyone seems to understand the situation is dire, regardless of the language barrier.

Mr Socially Superior, on the other hand, doesn't seem to understand anything. Ms Fat 'n Loud and Miss Well Travelled are trying to roll Mrs Socially Superior onto her side into the recovery position. Mr Socially Superior stands next to them uselessly, the drink bottles still in his hands, and does nothing to help. Mr Gay Man 1 looks over his shoulder, sees what is happening, taps his husband on the shoulder and they bend down to help get Mrs Socially Superior onto her side. Ms Fat 'n Loud checks her pulse and breathing.

Mr Socially Superior is completely out of his depth. He says lamely, "She'll be alright. She just needs a minute ..."

Ms Fat 'n Loud looks up at him with something akin to contempt and then addresses our group with a command. "I need water! And lots of it!" Suddenly, there are a dozen bottles of water being thrust at Ms Fat 'n Loud. She twists the caps off and pours the contents over the unconscious woman's body, then takes off her hat and starts fanning Mrs Socially Superior. Miss Well Travelled and Mr and Mr Gay Couple see what she is trying to do, remove their hats and use them as fans too.

Mrs Twinkling Eyes, Mrs Gentle Wit and I have a woozy Leslie safely sitting in a chair with water and potato crisps, which seem to appear out of nowhere, and are keeping watch over her while the drama unfolds before us.

Ms Fat 'n Loud looks up, grabs the impotent Mr Socially Superior and pulls him down onto his knees. She is really angry. "Now listen, you useless piece of crap! Your wife is having a heat triggered meltdown! If we don't get her body temperature down, she'll go into organ failure and die! Have you got that!" He nods, his face sagging as he understands this is for real. "I want you to keep pouring water over her and keep fanning her. Fan her, man, fan her!" Mr Socially Superior takes his hat off and starts fanning for all he's worth.

The cafeteria staff come to our aid. A carton of bottled water appears and our group remove the lids and pour water over our stricken comrade. Someone brings a small electric fan, someone else produces an extension chord, it is plugged in and Ms Fat 'n Loud holds it over Mrs Socially Superior's body. Ms Fat 'n Loud keeps checking her pulse and I can see her jaw setting. She is really worried.

We are all looking out for an ambulance to arrive, knowing that we are a three hour drive from Aswan. And then we hear a welcome sound above us. A helicopter arrives and lands in the car park outside. It is a military helicopter and a medivac

147

team gets out, is met by Mohamed and quickly comes to Mrs Socially Superior and Leslie.

The crowd is moved even further back and the medivac team go to work. They all speak English and work with Ms Fat 'n Loud to get an IV drip into Mrs Socially Superior and another into Leslie. Leslie is moved onto a stretcher and taken out to the helicopter while the rest of the team stabilise Mrs Socially Superior. After a few moments, they stretcher her out to the helicopter. It has all happened very quickly. I expect Egyptians are experts in dealing with heat stroke in tourists.

Mr Socially Superior seems to be left out of what is happening. He approaches the helicopter, but is stopped by Ms Fat 'n Loud who is about to climb on board. She snaps at him, "You go back to the ship and get some things for your wife! And get her passport and your travel insurance papers, you'll need them at the hospital!" He nods and steps back. Then the helicopter door slides shut, they take off and disappear into the distance. Mr Socially Superior is left standing alone in the car park.

The rest of us are standing around in shock and looking at each other. What now?

Well, one of us knows what now. Mrs Intelligentsia is shooting black looks at Mr Socially Superior. I think we should console him, but Mrs

Intelligentsia has other ideas. Something is brewing inside her and suddenly comes to the boil. She walks up to him and pokes him in the chest. "You should be ashamed of yourself!" He looks completely confused. "You should have seen how crook your wife was! You should have done something!" She pokes him again. He is speechless. As are the rest of us. Is the heat making her behave like this? No, it's not the heat. It's the post-menopausal, oestrogen-deprived, authoritative, controlling feminist in her. "I bet you haven't really seen your wife in years! Have you? I bet you couldn't even tell me what she is wearing today! Can you? I bet you take her for granted at home like a piece of furniture! She's just your housemaid, isn't she? Nothing more than an unpaid servant!"

Oh dear. Nobody knows what to do or say. This has caught us completely off guard. Mr Intelligentsia moves towards his wife to placate her, but she holds up her hand to stop him and snaps, "Stay!" He steps back like a well trained dog. I almost expect him to sit and bark. It's clear who wears the pants in this marriage. His wife is formidable! And she hasn't finished yet. She's poking Mr Socially Superior in the chest again. He'll have bruises for a week. "I should sic my friend Germaine on to you! She'd give you what for!"

Germaine? She couldn't be talking about THE Germaine, could she? The Mighty Greer herself?

She is.

"It's men like you that made my friend Germaine write 'The Female Eunuch'! I thought you lot had died out years ago, but you ... you!" She pokes him yet again. I wonder at what point her poking becomes assault.

Mr Socially Superior's face collapses under this verbal attack. He's used to bossing women around, especially his own wife. And now he's being held responsible for his wife's life and death crisis by, of all things, a woman. He simply doesn't know how to cope with someone like Mrs Intelligentsia.

Mohamed suddenly steps forward and calmly places himself between them. "Come, come. It is very hot and we are all upset. And it's time to get back on the bus," he says in his beautifully modulated voice. His words defuse the situation immediately. Mrs Intelligentsia steps back, unrepentant but aware she is not the authority here, Mohamed is. She joins her obedient husband.

I am relieved. We are all relieved. I wasn't sure where that little altercation was going to end up.

Mohamed continues, addressing Mr Socially Superior. "When we get back to Aswan, I'll arrange for you to be taken straight to the hospital. You'll naturally want to be with your wife."

150

Mr Socially Superior, all trace of smugness gone from his face, nods. And then he begins to tremble and cry. He is really scared. My heart goes out to him. And so do some other hearts. Hubby and Mr Gentle Wit go to him with reassurances and flank him protectively as we walk to the bus. They have one eye on Mrs Intelligentsia and the other on the weeping man between them. It's a humbling thing for a man to cry in public. And to be driven to tears by an angry woman you don't even know - there is no way of maintaining your male dignity in the face of that. Even if he did deserve it.

I think all the men are a little afraid of Mrs Intelligentsia now. I'm not. I agreed with her assessment of Mr Socially Superior. But now I'm sorry for him. Sometimes, people are who they are because they don't know any better. I expect that is true of him.

We board the bus in silence. Mr Socially Superior sits at the front with Mohamed. There is no conversation as the bus takes us to the decrepit plane, we board and know we need to endure another half hour of overheated airlessness.

And them someone has a clacker valve moment.

Oh, you don't know what a clacker valve is? It's that vital little sphincter muscle that controls the exit of intestinal gases. Farts to you and me. It's the reason we are called Old Farts in the first place, because when it goes, and it goes in all of us eventually, we become known for its failure. Even if someone else in the vicinity has farted, we will be blamed for it. Don't believe me? Just get into a crowded lift, wait for someone to fart and watch them all back away from you.

Joan Rivers used to joke a lot about getting old. My favourite one was that after 60, we cannot control our farts, but we do not lose our sense of smell until we enter our 70s, so between 60 and 70 is a perilous time for us Old Farts. We learn to manage it quite well, although walking is a major fail time. Walking signals the uncontrollable exit of many small, mostly silent farts and we need to walk fast enough to keep ahead of the smell. And look innocent at the same time. Never walk behind Old Farts in shopping centres. You'll regret it if you do. Sitting in theatres and cinemas is another clacker valve trap. We learn to lct it slip out slowly and keep our eyes fixed on the stage or screen, all the while knowing we are in the dark and cannot be identified later.

Seniors package tours with a lot of time spent on buses can be truly perilous. There are multiple small deadly explosions going on at seat level, but the good thing about modern tourist buses is that the airconditioning creates a pleasant stream of air at nose height and generally wafts the fart shock waves away fairly quickly, and most buses use air fresheners. We are all doing it, so we pretend not to notice and envy those who have already lost their sense of smell. It is something to look forward to.

But here we are on an old plane in stifling heat with no air-conditioning and no air circulating at all. We are trapped! And someone's tummy is not coping with the change in diet. It fills the small plane and hands go to noses. Hubby and I look at each other. No, it is not us. I take a couple of tissues from my handbag and hand one to Hubby. We hold them to our noses as unobtrusively as possibly and wait for it to pass. But it has nowhere to go. My eyes are starting to water. Goodness, what did the perpetrator eat last night? I have a sense of drowning as the fart fills the plane and I fervently hope we don't lose anyone else on this journey. We've just seen two of our group flown out, will there be more? Can there be Death by Fart? Where is Hercule Poirot when you need him?

Then I feel the plane begin to descend and watch intently as the desert below rises up to meet us and the plane touches down. It seems to roll on for an eternity before it stops. The front door is opened and - hallelujah - the crisis is over. We feel that cursed hot, gritty wind blow through and nearly weep for the relief of it.

We are to be shuttled by bus from the plane to the building. As we file out of the plane, still a little woozy from our clacker valve drama, I am stopped at the door. Apparently the shuttle bus can only take half of the passengers at a time and the rest of us must wait for it to return.

As I stand at the door of the plane, the door to the cockpit opens next to me. I glance idly into it and wish I hadn't.

Two pilots are sitting in the tiny cockpit, which is quite filthy. In contrast to the grime around them, the pilots are young, wearing immaculate navy and white uniforms, and speaking to each other in French. They have opened the door to speak to one of the flight attendants, who also speaks to them in French. They all look confident and unconcerned.

But they don't inspire confidence in me. The instrument panel inside the cockpit seems to be quite damaged and has been repaired and held together with what appears to be gaffer tape. If that isn't bad enough, the windows of the plane are cracked and glued roughly into their frames with some sort of grey adhesive, which is actually melting in the heat and dripping down the edges of the glass. The pilots' seats are so tattered that I can see the metal frame inside them.

Hubby behind me sees what I see and we look at each other in horror. Had we really just travelled

154

over the desert in this death trap? Hubby sees the look on my face and whispers in my ear, "Aren't you glad we didn't see that before we left?"

The shuttle bus returns, takes us to the airconditioned building, we board our proper bus and return to our ship in time for lunch.

Hubby and I go to our room for a shower and some soothing cream for my windburn. All the sunscreen in the world doesn't protect you from windburn. My face looks scoured and is stinging. I know it will be worse tomorrow, but there is nothing I can do other than apply the cream and go eat.

It is a very subdued group that joins the Brits in the dining room for a buffet lunch. I look for Mohamed. We need to know how our comrades are. We are afraid for them.

I see Mr Socially Superior and Mohamed through the window of the dining room. Mohamed is putting two suitcases into the boot of a taxi. It looks like a decision has been made to leave the tour. I can understand that. The taxi drives away, leaving Mohamed at the wharf.

A couple of the Brits come over to ask after our ailing comrades. They have heard about what happened. They are friendly and understanding. Old Farts are accustomed to crises. After all, every one of us has had practice of one sort or another. It simply goes with getting old.

We finish lunch and, as we settle down with our coffees, we feel the ship leave the wharf and move slowly along the water. We are going down the Nile, but having no sense of direction (it's a girl thing), I feel as if we are going up the Nile. If we are heading north, isn't that up? But the source of the Nile is south, so we are heading north towards the end of the Nile, which is downriver. Hubby explains it to me carefully, but I still feel like we are travelling upriver. Are you confused? I am. Even now.

Mohamed calls our group into the lounge area and gathers us around. He tells us that Leslie is fine and is being kept in hospital overnight for observation, (there is an audible sigh of relief from the women), but that Mrs Socially Superior will be in hospital for several days. She is stable, but not in very good shape. Her husband is being accommodated at the hospital and we probably won't be seeing either of them again, but we will be notified of Mrs Socially Superior's condition. Ms Fat 'n Loud is staying at the hospital overnight to support both her patients.

Ms Fat 'n Loud has the admiration of us all.

Then Mohamed smiles and tells us that it is a fortunate thing that he was called in at the last minute to join the Egyptian leg of our tour, or we would now be without a guide. We assumed his presence was pre-planned. No, he tells us, he was woken at midnight by a phone call from the tour company after our Meet and Greet in Cairo and joined us the next morning. Why? Because Leslie's wallet was stolen from her handbag at the Meet and Greet, and inside that wallet was the tour company's cash, credit cards, vouchers and other essential documents. Mohamed was called in to bring a replacement set of credit cards and cash.

I stifle a gasp. I knew it! I should have said something when I saw that wallet sticking out of the bag. It was an invitation to any thief within lurking distance. And I didn't know at the time that Leslie was pregnant and therefore had baby brain. That explains a lot.

Mohamed goes on to tell us that he agreed to stay the full week because he knew Leslie was pregnant and not feeling well. Apparently, Leslie is extremely embarrassed about losing her wallet after giving the standard lecture on security to us all. He asks that we not mention it when she returns. I exchange an amused glance with Mrs Twinkling Eyes and Mrs Gentle Wit. Fat chance! All of us mothers in the group know exactly what baby brain is. We'll give her heaps and make a joke out of it, rather than let her suffer an embarrassment that we've all known in one way or another when pregnant. Why, during one of my pregnancies, I took my dog for a walk on a lead - without the dog! I just dragged the lead along the footpath for a mile or so until I got to the park, where I went to let him off the lead - and realised I'd left him at home! No, we are going to have fun with Leslie. And we are also going to look after her. We don't need to discuss it. It's a maternal thing, women looking after pregnant women.

We are due to visit the Kom Ombi temple shortly, but Mohamed gives us the option of staying on board if we wish, as the morning's events have been rather stressful. It is no surprise to me that we all say we will go to the temple, even the Two Oldies who look exhausted. We can't do anything for our ailing comrades by sitting around and feeling sorry for them, and we will not be passing this way again. May as well get on with things. Old Farts are like that. You do what you can, when you can, then when you can't do anything more, you get on with things!

We go onto the upper deck and watch the banks of the Nile glide past us. The water is smooth and gleaming in the fierce heat. The temperature is a good ten degrees cooler on the water, but the humidity is much higher. I feel as if we are gliding through a hot, wet tunnel.

The Kom Ombi temple is a glorious sight as we approach it by river. I guess that it was built for that effect. We gather at the prow of the ship to watch it. Mr Twinkling Eyes says, "Another pile of rocks," and the now familiar chuckle passes through our group.

I don't need to go into too much detail about Kom Ombi, or any of the other magnificent places we see on our tour, because if you are reading this, you have either been there or you can Google the sights we see. This is not a travelogue, but rather a traveller-ogue.

I can say that the heat is still fierce but the wind less so, and Mrs Teetering Heels has come up with a good solution to her footwear problem. She leaves the ship and enters Kom Ombi with her flat sandals on, groaning in genuine pain, then as soon as the surface of the ground is level enough, she whips a pair of very high heeled sandals out of her husband's backpack and slips into them with relief. At which point her husband lends her his iron grip to keep her upright. They are back in familiar territory. Hubby and I exchange a private grin.

Mr and Mrs Effusive catch up with us. Mrs Effusive and I are openly excited about the temple. We remark on the many carved pictures on the walls and columns, the endless hieroglyphs covering every inch that the pictures miss and the hugeness of it all. I comment that it seems that the whole of Ancient Egypt was an illustrated book. I would love to be able to read the story.

Mohamed is behind us. He shows us a line of hieroglyphs and translates them. It is rather disappointing. It says something like, "two goats were ordered but only one was delivered", or "it is the first street on your left, the third house down", or something equally mundane. He sees the looks on our faces and laughs. Then he takes us to another section and there we hear him translate something about the gods Horus and Sobek and the wonderful afterlife that was promised to the pharaohs, regardless of how good or bad they were in this life. Mrs Effusive remarks that it sounds positively Catholic to her.

We are doing a lot of neck craning, as the temple walls and pillars are so high. Suddenly, Mrs Effusive gasps and points up to a relief on a pillar of a man with an unnaturally large phallus. We all follow her gaze. A titter goes through the females. Then she spots another such relief on the opposite pillar. This time we laugh outright. Mrs Effusive says what we are all thinking - well, the females amongst us anyway. "Looks like they're pointing them at each other!"

Young Oldie says, "Well, nothing has changed in five thousand years, has it? They're competing over who has the biggest willy."

I laugh so hard that tears roll down my cheeks, and even harder when Mohamed asks what "willy" means and Young Oldie points to the area of his groin under his galabeya. His eyes light up and he joins our laughter.

The rest of Kom Ombi is not clear in my mind as I write this. But those two reliefs on the pillars will never be forgotten.

We return to the boat, all exhausted. We have time for a nana nap in our cool rooms, then shower again and change for the galabeya party.

Hubby is dreading this. We are supposed to dress up in what Hubby calls "girl's gear". Mohamed has already assured the men that the galabeya is the coolest way to dress in the heat, but he recommends that they wear underpants under the galabeyas. There will be a belly dancer at the party tonight, and without underpants, their erections might show under the galabeyas. I stifle a laugh as Mohamed holds the front of his galabeya out to demonstrate. These Old Fart men should be so lucky! I want to suggest that they all take their Viagra first, but restrain myself.

There is a shop on board the ship. It sells tourist tat as well as clothing and some very good jewellery. We girls decide to go shopping for our own party outfits. I buy a beaded blue head scarf and an aqua belly dancing outfit that covers me from head to toe in layers of chiffon, sequins and crystal beads, and floats around me when I turn. It feels wonderful! I am so busy admiring myself in the small mirror in the shop that I don't notice what anyone else is buying. Then I see some gold sandals with lots of glittery decoration on them and I am set.

We hear a disturbance coming from the upper deck. We quickly get back into our normal clothes and follow the noise, to find that a dozen small boats have rowed out to our ship. On each boat are two Egyptian men with plastic bags holding galabeyas in many different colours and styles. They call out to get our attention. The men are already at the boat railings, looking down.

I find Hubby. He says, "They don't miss a trick, do they?"

"Well, they have to make a living, too," I say in defence of the men yelling their heads off below us. "Do you think they know about our party tonight?"

"Probably got brothers and cousins on board who tell them."

"Probably. Are you going to buy anything?"

Hubby looks at me as if I have said something stupid. "I don't think so."

A lot of bargaining is going on around us. It starts with the boat vendors throwing up a bag containing a galabeya and yelling out a price. "Ten Egyptian pounds!" The bag gets thrown back down with the response, "One Egyptian pound!" Up comes the bag again. "Nine Egyptian pounds!" Down it goes. "Two Egyptian pounds!"

We hear Mohamed behind us. "Do not pay more than two Egyptian pounds for anything."

We heed him. The bargaining goes on. As the bags get tossed back down, they miss the boats and many of them end up in the water. The vendors simply row towards the floating bag and scoop it up. After a few minutes, less bags are being thrown back down. Money goes down instead. Coins. I am amazed at what lengths the vendors will go to in order to prevent the coins from hitting the water. When some of the coins hit the water, the vendors dive after the coins before they disappear into the murky water. This is life threatening stuff going on here!

One of the bags is flung up and hits Hubby who is getting caught up in the fun. He's about to toss it back, but I grab it, open it and say, "Look. It's a man's galabeya. Black with gold trim. Looks like it might fit. You could wear it tonight."

Hubby takes the garment, holds it against himself, and we hear a voice from below yell, "Ten Egyptian pounds! Just for you! Good bargain just for you, sir!"

Hubby says to me, "Not bloody likely," pushes the garment back into the plastic bag and tosses

163

it back down. Up it comes again. "Ten Egyptian pounds for you, sir! It will make you look very handsome!"

We laugh. I say, "For goodness sake, make him an offer."

Hubby relents and looks down. "One Egyptian pound!" and down the bag goes. Up it comes again.

"Nine Egyptian pounds!"

"One!" Down it goes.

"Eight Egyptian pounds! Very good bargain for you, sir!" Up.

"One!" Down.

"Seven Egyptian pounds, sir! I must feed my children!" Up.

"One!" Down.

"Six Egyptian pounds! My children will not eat well tonight!" Up.

"One!" Down.

"Five Egyptian pounds! Think of my poor children!" Up.

"One!" Down.

"Four Egyptian pounds! My children! My children!" Up.

"One!" Down.

"Three Egyptian pounds! My wife will starve too!" Up.

"One!" Down.

"Two Egyptian pounds! My mother and my father will starve with my wife and my children!" Up.

"One!" At which point, Hubby tosses down a one Egyptian pound coin instead of the bag.

The vendor catches the coin, looks up at Hubby and says, "You a Scotsman, sir!" It isn't a question, it is a statement, and doesn't refer to Hubby's accent, which now is purely Australian, but to his bargaining. He got it so right. We still laugh about that.

Our ship docks at Edfu. There are market stalls lining the dock, with the usual cries of, "Very cheap, just for you!" and tourist tat being held out to tempt us. But we have other things on our mind. We are not going to leave the ship tonight. We are going to party on dude!

Hubby wears his black galabeya to the party with pride. After all, he only paid one Egyptian pound for it. Bargain! Even his golfer's legs don't worry him. Do I hear you say, "what are golfer's legs?" Well, for a start, they are usually well shaped due to all the walking. Eighteen holes of golf can cover several kilometres and Hubby plays a couple of times a week, as well as his daily early morning walks. He has more shapely calves than me. But during the warmer months, golfers wear shorts with their golf shoes and socks, and develop a tan between the bottom of their shorts and the top of their socks. Their feet and ankles are lily white below the well defined tan line.

So golfers don't have VPL (Visible Panty Line), they have VTL (Visible Tan Line). And that tan line is clearly visible below Hubby's galabeya. If it was two inches longer, it would be hidden. Hubby looks down and from that angle, he can't see his VTL. I can, though, but choose not to tell him. I think he looks very cute.

I dress in my authentic made-in-China Egyptian belly dancing dress, scarf and sandals, dab on a bit of party makeup, check it in the bathroom mirror and we leave for the party.

A group of Nubian musicians is playing drums and flutes and, thankfully, the room is dimly lit for atmosphere. Everyone is in costume of some description, with varying degrees of success, but we all look exactly like what we are - lumpy, bumpy Old Fart western tourists doing kitschy western touristy stuff. We are here for a good time and, damn it, that's just what we are going to have! We all dance and drink and pretend not to notice how silly we all look. After all, today was tough and we need to de-stress a bit. Even Ms Miseryguts has a small, tight smile on her face. It doesn't look right, but she's trying. I expect she's grateful that it's not her in hospital tonight.

Miss Know-it-all is locked in conversation with Mr Red Pants about the history of Abu Simbel. Apparently, her set of statistics differ from his. Mrs Red Pants sips her chilled white wine in silence, content that her husband is with her in mind as well as body tonight.

Mrs Love-a-Chat is sitting next to the Two Oldies, talking with her eyes closed, the way a former mother-in-law of mine used to do. I could leave the room, cook a three course meal, eat it, clean up and return to the room to find her still talking with her eyes closed and unaware that I'd even left the room. The Two Oldies sip their gin and tonics and ignore her. Everyone there is happy.

Miss Well Travelled is chatting with the 2 Texan Gals and Mr and Mr Gay Couple. Every time Texan Gal 1 raises her voice, Mr Gay Couple 2 gently touches her on the hand, which seems to act like a volume control so that she lowers her voice. Magic.

Mr and Mrs Intelligentsia are with Mr and Mrs Effusive. Mrs Effusive is being herself, effusive, and alcohol seems to encourage her. She is almost jumping out of her skin with the thrill of tonight's party. Mrs Intelligentsia keeps trying to make intelligent conversation, which Mrs Effusive simply over rides with her ... well, effusiveness!

Mr Intelligentsia has given up on trying to make conversation with Mr Effusive, who is not effusive but laconic to the point of being semi-conscious. And Mr Effusive is a beer man. He doesn't know wine and doesn't care. They have nothing to talk about. It suits both of them.

Mr and Mrs Teetering Heels are with the 3 Shopping Sisters. They are comparing the heels on their shoes. Mrs Teetering Heels wins by at least four centimetres. Mr Teetering Heels looks very relaxed. His wife is, after all, sitting down. He has no responsibility other than to be there. It's like a reprieve for him.

Hubby and I find ourselves with Mr and Mrs Twinkling Eyes and Mr and Mrs Gentle Wit. It wasn't a deliberate thing, we just gravitate towards each other naturally and find a table to put our drinks on. Then the musicians have a break, some 60's dance music is played, the mirror ball and disco lights come on and we hit the dance floor.

Hubby and I wriggle and jiggle around on the dance floor under the ultra violet disco lights, my dress floating and sparkling around me. I feel gorgeous. He suddenly stops me and says, "Did you check yourself in the mirror before?"

"Yes. Why? Have I got a booger or something?"

"Not exactly. Better go check though."

Oh gawd, what is wrong? I leave him and quickly go back to our room to check my reflection in the full length mirror on the back of the wardrobe door.

Damn! You can see through the layers of chiffon and it ain't a pretty sight! I may be an Australian size 12 and my weight may be within the healthy weight range, but you can see every lump, bump, stretch mark, surgical scar and bit of cellulite, as well as the big white granny knickers. They probably glowed under the ultra violet light.

I need my Spanx under this dress. I rummage around in the suitcase and find it. Another damn! I brought the black Spanx to wear under my black evening dress that I camouflage with a loose jacket anyway, so why do I need the Spanx in the first place? And why oh why didn't I pack the nude Spanx?

The Spanx starts just under my bra and finishes just above the knee. It looks ridiculous and even worse than the white undies through the flimsy chiffon. I can't wear black under this dress. Or can I? Maybe it won't be noticeable in the ultra violet light. I swirl around. Hhmm. I think it will do. The lesser of two evils. And at least I shouldn't glow in the dark.

I go back downstairs to the party just as the photographer does her rounds. Hubby and I pose for several photographs, then get back to our drinks and dancing.

The belly dancer arrives. I whisper to Hubby, "Got your knickers on?" He grins.

The belly dancer does her stuff and all the men look very disappointed. She is fat by western standards, but still slimmer than most of us Old Farts. Her belly hangs over her low slung, beaded belt, she has very little in the bosom department, and her dancing is rather uninspiring. She slowly gyrates around the room, giving each man a minute of personal attention, her belly moving in waves a few inches from their noses, an amused smile on her face.

I think she is doing exactly what a belly dancer should do - make her belly dance. But the men were expecting something out of a Hollywood movie with a Marilyn Monroe figure and the seductive powers of Rita Hayworth in Gilda. There are no worries about an accidental erection under their galabeyas. I glance at some of the other wives and we are all looking amused and knowledgeable. Our men might even find us more attractive after this.

The Brits, who are gathered across the other side of the room from us, look positively bored. They've seen it all before and just get on with their drinking.

The belly dancer leaves and a Whirling Dervish comes on. He is a very handsome young man with long black hair tied back in a ponytail. His costume is a yellow skirt trimmed with scarlet beads. He begins to spin and the skirt flairs out. He spins faster and faster and just when we think he can't get any faster, he flips his flared skirt up over his head and spins so fast that our eyes cannot process it. He does amazing things with balancing decorated wooden plates whilst continuing to spin and flare the skirt out. Then he slows for a moment and we think the dance is almost over. But not so. He speeds up again, taking his hair out of the ponytail to let it fly out around his head. And then he does something that freaks us all out. As he spins, he moves his head from side to side and for a few minutes, he looks headless, only black hair flying out above his shoulders. As Dame Edna would say, it is spooky! Then he slows and finally ends his dance to unanimous applause.

We fall into bed quite late, aware that the morrow brings two more temple visits, but leisure time aboard the ship as well. Two more temples. Two more piles of rocks and some time out. Sounds good!

DAY 7

LUXOR TEMPLE

I awake with my face stinging from the previous day's windburn. My reflection in the mirror is scary. I am going to blister, damn it! Makeup will be out of the question for several days, not that it was ever a priority for me anyway.

We arrive at breakfast to find the room half empty. It would appear that some of our group are down with Cairo Tummy, including Mr and Mrs Twinkling Eyes. Some of the Brits are missing, too. We eat warily, hoping it isn't the food. It shouldn't be. It's more likely the Nile water in our bathrooms. We've been told that it doesn't take more than a few drops to work its evil on westerners, and we have already heard from several members of our group that they have been brushing their teeth with it. They believe it will only make them sick if they ingest it. I expect they are revising that belief this morning.

After breakfast, we are told our photos from the previous evening are ready to inspect. Hubby and I go to the onboard shop to get ours, and I am horrified, truly horrified. My black Spanx are clearly visible through the aqua chiffon dress, not to mention the beaded head scarf covering one eye. My face is so bright red from the windburn that I glow. I look ridiculous! Hubby jokes that I look like an advertisement for an Egyptian brothel (my face is glowing like a red light according to him), but it is no worse than his white feet below his VTL poking out from the bottom of his black galabeya. He asks me why I didn't tell him how silly he looked. I just smile, kiss him and tell him he looked very sexy to me, and didn't he think I looked sexy last night too? He glances at me and says dutifully, "Yes, dear." He's such a good husband.

We have a giggle and agree that these photos will never come out to be seen. We take them back to the cabin and I tuck them away inside my suitcase.

And when we get home, I find them again and they make me laugh. It was a memorable night, we had fun despite the day's difficulties, and with my perverse sense of humour, I feel the need to display them. I choose the worst of the photos, frame it and there it stands on our sideboard to this day. One red faced, pudgy, plain, grey haired Old Fart in a see-through dress displaying my black Spanx and with one eye covered by a silly scarf, making me look like a deranged pirate. And one balding, pot bellied Old Fart in a too short black galabeya with tanned calves and white feet sticking out underneath and, sadly for him, no erection showing through his galabeya. The best part, though, is our big smiles. Gotta laugh!

Although we are feeling tired, we join the remnants of our group as we board the bus to visit the Temple of Horus at Edfu. It is magnificent and when Hubby jokes in the absence of Mr Twinkling Eyes, "Another pile of rocks," our group chuckles. It has become a catchphrase.

As we wander around the temple, Miss Well Travelled, who is very savvy about avoiding Cairo Tummy and therefore still with us, points out a particular relief to me. It is of a woman breastfeeding her baby. I wish Leslie was here to see it. But then, she's seen it before. Although it might mean more to her now. It is timeless and beautiful. We hope all is well with Leslie.

Back on the ship, we make ourselves comfortable on the upper deck and watch every day life on the banks of the Nile slide past us as we drift down stream to Luxor. Hubby and I comment on the startling contrast between the narrow strip of fertile green on both river banks against the backdrop of the seemingly endless desert. We see men on donkeys pulling old carts with fresh produce, just as they have been doing for thousands of years. We see children down on the river bank, splashing around in the water. We see women doing the family washing in the same water that someone is shitting in just metres from them. We see many people and, as we glide past them, all of them, without exception, stop to wave to us. We hear them call out "Hello!" and we wave back. It is marvellous!

Luxor comes into view. As we dock, there are several other floating hotels in front of us. And we experience a small reality check.

Hubby and I had given some laundry to one of the boat boys the previous evening. It would be returned to us, clean and pressed, this afternoon. We had imagined a modern laundry with washing machines and dryers working overtime to keep up with the passengers' washing. It is so cheap on the boat, compared to prices at hotels, and so nice not to have to do our smalls in the bathroom sink and find places to hang them all to dry.

As our ship docks behind another very similar vessel, we see several boat boys on the vessel in front of us sitting on some steps that go down into

175

the water at the back of the boat. And they are hand washing the passengers laundry in the Nile water. Lines are strung across the stern, loaded with items drying in the heat. Bras, undies, socks, shorts, dresses, trousers, jeans, t-shirts - it is all there. No washing machines. No dryers. Just man power - or boy power. Now we know why it is so cheap. I tell Hubby to remind me not to suck on my undies (not that I normally do anyway) as they have been washed in the deadly Nile water. He laughs. I'm not laughing though. I'm thinking of our undies, our very personal undies with our very personal stains, being handled and washed by young boys. Oh dear.

Those of our group who are not upchucking in their rooms are gathered up and taken to the Temple of Luxor. We are down to ten by now. I'm feeling pleased with myself that I have been so careful. And of course, Hubby of the Steel Gut never gets these sorts of things anyway, which is very handy for when I do. It helps to have someone to look after you.

Mohamed explains how this magnificent temple was lost for centuries under desert sand and rubble. Our small group is looking at Hubby expectantly. He embellishes a little. "Another pile of rocks under a pile of rocks." His comment is met with approving smiles.

We are overcome by the majesty of this place, as we have been overcome by so much in Egypt. We do not regret visiting it, despite the fact that my face is now peeling and raw, and the heat is making us both feel drained. Along with about a thousand other tourists, we pass through the entrance and stroll along at our own pace. Our group disperses into the crowd, but that is fine as we know to converge outside the temple again at a certain time.

Mr and Mrs Red Pants are walking behind us, the dog lead firmly in place. Mr Red Pants has been fine since the pyramid episode and I expect we have all become a little complacent, but I hear a sudden commotion and turn to see what is causing it.

Mr Red Pants is pulling his wife along and heading for the statue of a youthful Tutankhamun and his half-sister bride Ankhesenamun. Despite being quite damaged, the statue is still beautiful and quite moving. As we watch, Mr Red Pants clambers onto the statue. His wife pulls him back, but he is simply bigger and stronger than her and, instead, pulls her along with him. She is saying as gently as she can in such urgent circumstances, "No, dear, you mustn't climb up there..." But he ignores her. In fact, he seems oblivious to everything around him and focussed on something we can't see.

We go to Mrs Red Pants' aid quickly. Hubby reaches up to pull Mr Red Pants down while I add my weight to the pressure on the dog lead. Her arm is stretched to its full limit and I can see it is hurting her. And then Mr Red Pants does a little twist and lies himself across the laps of the young Pharaoh and his Queen and ... oh no ...oh please not that ... he wraps his mouth around the marble breast of the girl bride and begins to suck. He is breastfeeding!

Mrs Red Pants is beside herself. She looks around and sees Mohamed coming towards us at a trot. And I look around and see hundreds of tourists laughing and taking photos on their cameras and phones. It's not like you could miss Mr Red Pants in his red pants above the heads of the crowd. The air is alive with flashes and laughter and amused chatter. I hear someone say, "It must be a publicity stunt." Someone else says, "Where is the film crew? There must be a film crew."

Mohamed joins Hubby and they carefully prise Mr Red Pants off the nipple and pull him down from the statue. He reaches out towards it and whispers pitifully, "Mummy?" and I nearly cry. Mohamed says to Hubby, "It is alright, sir, I will take care of this," and quickly guides Mr and Mrs Red Pants through the crowd, who are still taking photos and videos.

I just know this will go viral. I only hope none of the Red Pants family or friends will see it. Mrs Red Pants looked mortified. I would be too. Poor things.

Hubby and I take a deep breath and keep going. But our minds are on our new friends and their dilemma. And the image of Mr Red Pants sucking hungrily on that 4,300 year old breast is burned into our brains forever.

We welcome our return to the ship where Mohamed informs us all that Mr Red Pants is sedated and resting. Mrs Red Pants will remain in the room with him for the rest of the day. Our group discusses it quietly and respectfully, then we get on with our own itinerary. It is time for coffee, wine and iced tea and we make our way upstairs.

To our delight, Ms Fat 'n Loud is back. We enquire after our missing comrades. She tells us that Leslie has decided to leave the tour and go back home to rest. This sounds like a good idea to all of us, but we express our regret that we did not get the chance to thank her and say goodbye. Then I remember that we all have Leslie's mobile number in our phone contact list. We decide to send her text messages to wish her well for her wedding and the baby's birth.

Then Ms Fat 'n Loud informs us all that Mrs Socially Superior is recovering well and should be out of hospital in a couple of days. We are very happy to hear that. She adds, "As for that waste of space she is married to, I think he's had quite a wake up call! Frightened the bejeezus out of him!"

And so it should.

As the evening approaches, a couple more of our group begin to feel sick and dinner that night is a small affair, until the Brits invite us to join them.

Now, Brits on holiday, especially Old Fart Brits, really know how to relax. It is helped along with copious amounts of alcohol and food and a lot of talk about nothing in particular. Usually, they are complaining about something. The food, the plumbing, the heat, the cold, the people. They are known as Whinging Poms in Australia. But not this group. Every one of them has retired after years of working and raising families and paying off mortgages. We all have that in common. And we all know we are well off because we are still alive, we can afford to be here and we are enjoying ourselves.

Hubby, being British born but Australian by choice, fits in straight away and is delighted to find another Scotsman with a taste for Glenfiddich Whisky. As the dinner progresses, Hubby's acquired Australian accent seems to morph into the Scottish brogue of his childhood and, before I know it, he's reciting Robert Burn's "Address to a Haggis". He pronounces Robert as "Rabbie" and his accent gets thicker and thicker as he recites:

> "Fair fa' your honest, sonsie face,
> Great chieftain o' the puddin-race!
> Aboon them a' ye tak your place,
> Painch, tripe, or thairm:
> Weel are ye wordy of a grace
> As lang's my arm."

And so on and so forth. The Brits applaud and I lean over and whisper to him, "I didn't understand a word, but it sounds sexy." His eyes light up. We are in "the mood" and it must not be wasted. We make our excuses and go back to our room. I go into the bathroom for a quick bladder call and when I emerge a couple of minutes later, Hubby is lying on the bed. Sound asleep and snoring loudly. I should have known. Old Farts and alcohol mean no hanky panky and too much snoring. Oh well. At least our intentions were good.

DAY 8

LUXOR, THEBES AND THE
VALLEY OF THE KINGS

I expect Hubby to be a bit hung over the next morning, but he has the constitution of a true Scotsman where alcohol is concerned and seems fine. Not so me. If one of us snores at home, we have a guest room at the other end of the house to escape to. Here, on the ship, there is no escape and so I spent the night tossing and turning next to a noise that sounded like grating gears on a truck.

Hubby tells me that I snore like a steam train trying to climb a mountain. I didn't know what he meant until he recorded me one night. I do sound like a steam train trying to climb a mountain! Hence the relegation to separate rooms when we occasionally snore. We know quite a few Old Fart couples who permanently sleep in separate rooms because of snoring, or sleep apnoea, or tossing and turning. If you want to live a long healthy life, sleep is essential!

At breakfast, Hubby tucks into his food while I tuck into several cups of coffee to kick start me. We need to get back to our room in time to pack up our suitcases and have them outside our room door before we get on the bus. We are leaving our dream Nile cruise and flying back to Cairo this evening.

One of the most attractive things about a seniors package tour like ours is that so much is taken care of - the hotel bookings, the best sights to see, the language differences, to tip or not to tip dilemma, getting from A to B without any hassles, the mysteries of currency conversion for the conversion-confused like myself, and of course, the handling of the luggage. Luggage was one of the reasons we moved on from self-drive holidays overseas to package tours. No more dragging heavy suitcases onto buses and trains and connecting flights, up stairs in dodgy hotels that advertise lifts but don't have them, down dusty lanes to B&Bs that look great online, but have bathrooms the size of postage stamps. No, on a good package tour, our luggage is taken care of from the moment we join the tour until the moment we leave it. We hand it over at the airport, when we get to our rooms, it is waiting for us outside the door, and when we leave, it is taken who knows where to turn up at the next hotel. Couldn't do it any other way now.

Most of our group is at breakfast this morning, having taken their over-the-counter antibiotics and recovered from their tummy wogs. Even Mr and Mrs Red Pants seem to be back to normal. No one mentions the episode of the previous day. We wonder if Mr Red Pants is even aware it happened, for this morning he is waxing lyrical about the wonders of Thebes and the Valley of the Kings.

We go back to our rooms for our morning ablute and our medications. When we packed our meds at home, we both put a week's worth into a tablet organiser and the remaining bottles and boxes into a bag. It is time to top up the tablet organiser. We sit on the bed, surrounded by our own personal pharmacy and Hubby discovers, to his horror, that one of his heart meds is missing. It was in a small bottle and contained enough for the entire trip. We search both suitcases, the bathroom, the bedding, the floors, every pocket and finally have to admit that it is missing. The only explanation is that it fell out when his suitcase broke.

Damn. Hubby needs that medication and, in Australia, it is prescription only. We will need to see a doctor and get a new prescription. Can we even do that in Egypt? Hubby pops his doctor's letter into his pocket, we put our suitcases outside our room and we go looking for Mohamed.

He smiles reassuringly and says, "You must see a pharmacist."

Hubby says, "But we need a prescription..."

"In Egypt, many medicines do not need a prescription. There is a pharmacy nearby. I will show you the way."

We are doubtful, but we trust Mohamed and follow him off the ship onto the dock. He points to the right. "Do you see that gate at the end of the road?"

We peer into the morning glare and can just make out a black gate that looks rather high and wide, like you would find at a foreign embassy. I was expecting a garden gate. We can not see any buildings beyond.

"You will ask at the gate. They will direct you."

They? I peer again and can see two figures flanking the gate.

"Go," Mohamed says cheerfully, "we will not leave without you." He waves us on and we dutifully obey.

As we get closer to the gate, I see the two figures take shape and my stomach knots. They look like security guards in black uniforms, both tall, broad shouldered and fit, and they are carrying guns. Big guns. Assault rifles, to be exact. Gawd what are we getting ourselves into here? All we want is a little tablet.

I link hands with Hubby and we approach the guards. They seem quite relaxed. Well, you would be, wouldn't you, if you were tall and wearing a black uniform and carrying a bloody big gun? And the two people coming towards you are little, old and leaking nervously into their incontinence pads. They watch us with unsmiling faces.

Hubby clears his throat. "Excuse me. We are looking for a pharmacy."

And suddenly, one of the guards grins broadly and says in perfect English, "You need medicines, sir? There is a pharmacy through there," and he points to a dirt track passing between rows of fruit trees. We cannot see what is beyond.

I say, "Is it far? We need to be back on the ship..."

"It is not so far. Just a short walk."

The second guard opens the gate for us and we pass through. Are we sweating from the heat or from anxiety? Perhaps a little of both.

We walk along the track without looking back. We cannot see any buildings as the track winds its way through orchards and fields. This is not what we had expected. In Cairo, where we bought our just-in-case Cairo Tummy antibiotics, the pharmacy was on a busy road amongst many busy shops. Here, there is no sign of habitation at all. My stomach is knotting up. I feel isolated and vulnerable.

We keep walking and up ahead we see what appears to be a garden around a small house. It doesn't look like a pharmacy, but as we get closer, we see the familiar green cross over the doorway. We look around. There are no other buildings in sight. We go in.

And we couldn't be more surprised. It's as familiar as any chemist shop at home. Rows of the usual pharmacy stuff, ranging from shampoo and makeup to cough and cold medications to bandages and suppositories. The labels look different, the language on the packs is Arabic, but the pictures look the same anywhere in the world. A red throat for lozenges, a miserable looking man clutching his belly for constipation, a smiling face for condoms. And so on and so forth. We walk to the back of the shop and see a woman behind the counter. She is in her mid thirties, dark haired and wearing a long linen shift over trousers and sandals, and a beautiful hijab of emerald green. Behind her is a boy of about eight or nine, sitting at a desk with a computer.

The woman looks up as we approach and says in English, "Hello. You are English? American?"

I say, "Australian."

Her smile widens. "Ah, then you do not mind the heat so much?"

"No, used to it."

Hubby says, "Bit hot for me."

I say, "He was born in Scotland."

She purses her lips and says sympathetically, "I am sorry."

I want to laugh.

She continues, "May I help you with something?"

Hubby takes the doctor's letter from his pocket and hands it to her. "I've lost one of my medications. It's the blood pressure tablet, but it is prescription only in Australia."

She is reading the letter. "It is this medication?" She points to one of the meds on the doctor's list.

"Yes, that's the one. Is there a doctor..."

"Oh, no need for a doctor. It is different in Egypt. I can give you that without a prescription."

"You can? That would be great."

"How many do you need?"

"About six or seven weeks?"

"That is no problem."

I look at the boy and he glances up at me cheerfully. I say, "Is that your son?"

She nods her head. "He is home from school today. He had a belly ache this morning, but he is fine now. I think his belly ache was because he had a maths test today. You know how boys are."

I nod. I raised several myself. "I know. Staying home is what makes them better. Doesn't hurt them to have a day off occasionally. And there will be other maths tests."

She chuckles as she turns towards the wall of tablets behind her.

I say, "Your English is excellent."

"I learned it in school. All Egyptian children learn English. It is very useful to us."

Hubby says, "And to us. Makes travel here so easy." He looks around the shop. There is a big sign suspended from the ceiling, so big it dominates the shop. He nudges me. I look up and say, "You sell Viagra here?"

She turns back to us with two tablet boxes in her hand. "Oh yes, we sell a lot of Viagra. Do you want some?"

Hubby looks uncomfortable. "No, it's fine, I was just curious..."

"It is very cheap here..."

"No, really..."

She has turned back to the wall of tablets. "It is only 4 Egyptian pounds a tablet here, but there is a cheaper one..."

Hubby is stunned. "4 Egyptian pounds? It's nearly 20 Australian dollars a tablet at home! That's...that's..."

"That is 275 Egyptian pounds. I have heard that it is very expensive in other countries."

Hubby hasn't recovered from the shock yet. "And you say there is a cheaper version?"

"Oh yes. Only 1 Egyptian pound per tablet, but it is not as good as Viagra."

Hubby's eyes are as wide as saucers.

I say, "Do you sell much Viagra?"

She laughs. "I sell many many Viagra. All Egyptian men take Viagra. Egyptian men are very horny."

Yep. She actually said that.

Hubby and I look at each other and laugh with her. She puts Hubby's tablets in a bag and takes the credit card. It is almost as cheap as the Viagra.

I say, "You seem rather isolated here."

"Oh no, I am very busy. There are many farmers and labourers nearby."

I have to ask. "Those armed security guards at the gate. What are they there for?"

"That is to keep the tourists out of the farms. Tourists are very curious people and don't understand that not all of Egypt is for them to walk around. But you must not be afraid. I do not think the guards have bullets in their guns. They would not want to shoot a tourist. They would lose their jobs if they shot a tourist." She grins at us. I think I love her.

We thank her for the tablets and walk back to the ship. As we pass through the open gate, we see the bus pull up next to our ship and we walk a little faster. Hubby is shaking his head. "Only 1 Egyptian pound. Only 1! Why that's...that's 6 or 7 cents a tablet!"

I chuckle. "Do you want to go back and stock up?"

"No. I don't think so. Do you think I should?"

"If you want to."

He looks at his watch. "Nah. No time. We have to get back to the ship. Don't want to hold the bus up."

"Sure?"

"Yeah. Sure."

We walk toward the bus. But Hubby looks a little regretful. Opportunity missed.

I say, "Are you going to tell the other blokes about the cheap Viagra?"

He shakes his head vehemently. "Nah. No need for that."

I don't have to ask him why. Men do not like to admit to other men that they need Viagra. Subject closed.

Our first visit this morning is to Thebes and if I thought it was hot yesterday, today is a furnace with a nasty gritty wind. I am greasy with sunscreen, which stings my windburnt face and is a magnet for the windborn grit to stick to. I decide not to worry about it. After all, women pay a fortune for mineral makeup, it's all the rage, and you can't get more mineral than a layer of desert sand sticking to your face.

Mohamed rounds us up. We hear, "Oh no, more steps," and by now, it's kind of endearing. She really can't help herself, it's a phobia and we all have them to some degree or other. With me, it's lifts. Hate them. Have been claustrophobic since childhood. Got stuck in a lift once in the middle of Sydney. The emergency phone didn't work, no one took any notice of the alarm that I kept pressing and it was nearly an hour before I was released. The lift was one of those old, small, dark ones and I felt entombed. I was a mess by the time the lift mechanic prised the doors open. Had to take the rest of the day off work. I only get in lifts now if someone else is with me. So if Texan Gal 1 wants to complain about a couple of steps, let her. Who knows how she got to be that way? Everyone has a story to tell. Perhaps she'll tell us hers before the trip is over.

Our bus this morning is deliciously cool. The bottles of water kept at the front of the bus are chilled and our spirits are high. Our bus pulls into a tourist bus park and we get out to take photos of the Colossi of Memnon. Mr Effusive says laconically, "Big buggers. Need a bit of mortar, hey but." You can tell he's a northerner by the "hey but". Makes no sense to anyone south of the Queensland and Northern Territory borders. Even the ones who say it don't know what it means. But they say it constantly.

Mrs Effusive will not have her excitement dampened by her husband's dampening ways. "But you can see how they were built! How the rocks were cut and assembled and how they carved the statue from that. Clever, hey but?"

"Still could do with a bit of mortar."

Mrs Effusive clicks away madly with her camera. So do I.

We can see the Valley of the Kings in the distance. I am excited to be visiting that.

We pile back into the bus, refresh with chilled water and drive to the Valley of the Kings. And wait for something to appear. A tomb. An archaeological dig. A temple. Something. Anything. It is the most barren, uninspiring, rocky place and the road is rough. And then Mohamed explains why it was chosen to bury the kings in, about life beginning where the sun god rose on the fertile eastern side of the Nile and ending where the sun god set over the barren desert on the western side. The very landscape of the Valley of the Kings represents the end of life. And it all makes sense. Sort of.

We stop at the tourist centre, which is pretty much a hot tin shed full of hot tourists like ourselves. We dash to the loo, then shuffle around, looking for a bit of shade, until a local guide joins us to take us to one of the tombs open to the public. He is young, perhaps in his early twenties, with beautiful dark skin that does not burn in the sun and a welcoming smile that reveals perfect white teeth. He tells us to take it slowly, which is the Egyptian way, and all will be well. And to be sure we are wearing sensible shoes. He makes a joke about female Japanese tourists wearing high heels and I hear a scuffle behind me. It is Mrs Teetering Heels quickly changing into her flat sandals.

It is about a half kilometre walk along a rough, rocky track to the tomb and uphill all the way. I wait for someone to complain, but everyone's energy is totally consumed with not tripping on the rough ground and on surviving the unrelenting heat. Even Mrs Love-a-Chat and Ms Miseryguts are quiet. Just breathing is hard work, let alone talking. I see that Mohamed is between The Two Oldies, his strong arms guiding them over the uneven surface, their slow steps setting the pace for the rest of us. The young guide at the front of our group looks cool and sure footed in his white galabeya. He inspires confidence. If he hasn't expired in the heat, surely we won't either.

Finally, we are at the tomb. We could have walked past it and missed it, had it not been for the small fence around it. It is literally a hole tucked discreetly into the side of the rock face. A rather small hole. With a padlocked gate. The guide unlocks it and ushers us in.

Ms Miseryguts looks into the hole and says, "I'm not going in there."

Mohamed says gently, "You may wait here, but you will be alone."

She looks around at the empty hills and says, "Is it far? To the end?"

"Not so far, and there are lights all the way down. It is up to you."

Texan Gal 1 says, "Are there steps?"

The guide says, "No steps, madam. A very smooth floor all the way down."

Texan Gal 1 smiles with pleasure.

We enter the tomb in single file in no particular order. About four metres in, I hear Ms Fat 'n Loud's voice behind us declare, "I'm too fat for that narrow tunnel! I'll stay up here!"

Ms Miseryguts is two or three people behind me and says, "Oh, I'll go back and stay with her."

But it is too late. The tunnel is so narrow that there is not enough room for one person to pass another. We must go down as a group in single file and come back up the same way. It slopes down at about a 15 degree angle, not so bad, but the roof is so low that all of us, even little Ms Miseryguts, must bend our knees and duck our heads as we move forward. She turns to go back, realises she can't and resignedly continues on, muttering all the way.

And then begins a descent that my thighs have never forgotten. Once we started, we had to keep going. And going. And going. I had thought it would be just a few metres, but it was a long way down. We were going deep into the heart of the rocky hill. As we descend, the air becomes thick and fetid and the sweat is pouring off me. I had thought I was reasonably fit, but my knees and thighs are telling me otherwise. The descent is lit by a series of low wattage bulbs strung along the length of the tunnel, but they light it so dimly that we all have to concentrate on where we put our feet in the semi-darkness. We grip the handrail that runs along one wall and push on. I wonder how The Two Oldies are coping. I can hear puffing, panting and gasping, and of course, Ms Miseryguts whinging without end. Behind her, Mrs Love-a-Chat is rattling on about the price of milk at home or some such thing.

Suddenly, I hear Miss Know-it-all say, "Oh for goodness sake, both of you shut up! You're using up our oxygen!"

Ms Miseryguts and Mrs Love-a-Chat shut up. For now.

Finally, I see a brighter light up ahead and the tunnel opens into a chamber. There are bench seats around the edge of the chamber and we all head for them. A smaller chamber can be seen through a low doorway and it contains the big stone sarcophagus that the Pharaoh's mummy would have lain in. It is hotter and more fetid here than I could have imagined. I look around and no one has the breath to speak. And then I look up.

Oh my! The wall murals look as fresh as the day they were done. Well, at least they do to me. I am sure they glowed in the dark back in the day, but they are still glorious to behold. Gold and blue and black and white figures. The Pharaoh's life told in pictures. I can't remember now which Pharaoh it was, but I seem to recall the guide mentioning one of the Ramses, and his story is laid out before us, looking heroic on a gold chariot, hunting with a bow and arrow, fishing with a spear, victorious in battle as he stands over the bodies of his enemies, being worshipped by his subjects and slaves, being adored by his queen and children, sailing into the Afterlife with his servants, animals and possessions around him. It is all there and I know I cannot take it all in, but I want to. I remember seeing a book about this tomb in the tourist shop and determine to buy it before we leave.

The guide talks on and on about this particular Pharaoh, but I am beginning to feel a little sick and thick headed from the bad air and heat and so am not taking it all in. And then I notice The Two Oldies. They have risen from the bench seat and are edging past the guide towards the small chamber. I nudge Hubby and we watch the two women duck their heads and go through the low doorway. There are no wall murals inside that little chamber and there is barely standing room between the sarcophagus and the walls. What are they doing? I cannot resist. I rise and quietly follow The Two Oldies, Hubby behind me.

Inside the small chamber, The Two Oldies are walking around the sarcophagus, running their hands over the lid. As they come to a corner, Old Oldie says softly, "Here. There is a bit missing here."

Hubby and I go to see. One corner of the lid has a small piece chipped out of it, creating a hole about the size of a 50 cent piece. Young Oldie peers into the hole and whispers, "It is big enough." Then she reaches inside her handbag and takes out a bulging grey plastic bag.

Hubby and I look at each other. WTF?

198

I say, "What are you doing?"

Young Oldie says, "I'm burying my husband."

I want to gasp, but there isn't enough air.

Young Oldie continues matter-of-factly. "This is a place for dead people. He is dead."

Hubby glances over his shoulder at the rest of the group who are occupied with listening to the guide and says uncertainly, "Can you do that?"

Young Oldie smiles a little. "Just watch me." She holds the bag over the hole and nods to Old Oldie, who produces a small pair of nail scissors from her handbag and snips the corner of the grey plastic bag. Grey ash begins to flow from the bag, through the hole and into the sarcophagus. Young Oldie smiles broadly. "My children could not agree what to do with his ashes. There was such an argument, I cannot tell you how ugly it all got. Anything I suggested was ignored. My opinion didn't count." She paused as the bag emptied and she quickly put it back in her handbag. "So I decided to do it without them."

She looks up at us. "My husband was a prince. He was the love of my life and the king of our little castle on the farm. We had always wanted to visit Egypt together." She rests her hand on the sarcophagus. "And now we have, and he is buried amongst the pharaohs in a king's tomb. It is fitting. And he would have loved it." She smiles and patted the sarcophagus. Old Oldie puts her arm around her new friend and gives her an understanding squeeze.

If I wasn't so dehydrated, I'd be weeping. We are all deeply moved. We stand silently for a moment, then the guide's voice calls us back to the task of returning to the surface. We move back into the main chamber as unobtrusively as we had left it.

As we bend and awkwardly begin our uphill exit, I hear Old Oldie say, "You must find someone to bring your ashes here and mix them with his."

Young Oldie says, "I will ask my granddaughter. She travels a lot. She will do it."

And I find myself hoping she does.

The slow uphill trek is hell and when we reach the open air, my legs are trembling so badly I can hardly stand. I hang on to Hubby, but he isn't much better off. Everyone is hanging on to someone. We are a miserable sight. And I can hardly believe how cool and refreshing the hot gritty wind now feels, compared to what we had just left behind us.

We see two young Egyptian boys coming towards us with boxes under their arms. They put the boxes down, open them up and - hallelujah - they are full of bottles of cold iced tea and lemonade. Mohamed tells us to drink as much as we like, and he downs two in a few gulps. We lean against the shady side of the rock face and wait for our legs to behave, but

200

it is clear that is not going to happen in a hurry, so we all begin the unsteady walk back to the bus.

I hear the tap tap tap of The Two Oldies' walking sticks behind us and smile to myself. We have just witnessed the burial of a prince, a king, a much loved husband in the Valley of the Kings in Egypt, just as families and friends had witnessed the burial of their beloved husband/father Pharaohs thousands of years ago. How many people today can say that?

The bus awaits us. Hubby and I are the first two to board. The driver turns on the air conditioner as we sit down, then he stands and puts a new air freshener in the dispenser above him. A scent of cool pine needles wafts through the bus as the 2 Texan Gals board. They sit directly opposite us and immediately, Texan Gal 1 cries out, "Oh no, my allergies!"

Hubby and I look towards her as she digs around in her handbag to retrieve a paper face mask, the disposable sort you can buy during hayfever season in any chemist shop. She pops it on and cries out again, "I am getting a mee-graine! A mee-graine!"

I realise she believes she is allergic to the air freshener. Texan Gal 2 pats her on the hand and says reassuringly, "You took your antihistamine this morning, dear, you'll be alright."

"But I'm getting a mee-graine! Tell him to turn it off! That smell! Turn it off!"

Texan Gal 2 looks at us with resignation and rises to speak quietly to the bus driver. He removes the air freshener and shoots a bemused glance at Texan Gal 1, but he says nothing. He's an experienced driver, he's seen all sorts of tourists with their complaining, precious ways.

Ms Know-it-all boards and says, "Mmm, nice smell."

"It's giving me a mee-graine!"

Ms Miseryguts boards and says, "They should have told us what it would be like down there. They should have warned us..."

"It's giving me a mee-graine! A terrible mee-graine!"

Someone is actually complaining more than Ms Miseryguts and she isn't sure she can compete, so she quietly goes to her seat.

"It's still giving me a mee-graine! Get that air freshener off the bus!" And I think I will hit her if she says it one more time.

Ms Fat 'n Loud boards, looms over the Two Texan Gals and states in her booming voice which I have come to love, "It's more likely that you got your migraine from being overheated and dehydrated than that piddling little air freshener! Just take your meds and get over it!" She does not wait for a response, but moves to the back of the bus to take her seat.

Texan Gal 1 fishes around in her bag again and takes a couple of tablets, pulling her face mask down briefly to pop them into her mouth. Then she looks out of the window with a fixed stare. She has been told off by Ms Fat 'n Loud and she didn't like it. Texan Gal 2 comforts her with a little pat on the arm, then settles into her seat.

I glance sympathetically at Texan Gal 2. She leans across the aisle towards me and whispers, "She fell down some stairs when she was seven. Broke four ribs, both arms and fractured her skull. Unconscious for two weeks. She was very sick for a long time and she's suffered from anxiety ever since."

I make a silent, "Oh" and nod understandingly. I knew there had to be a story to Texan Gal 1's phobia. I turn to whisper to Hubby, but he has heard and shoots Texan Gal 2 a sympathetic smile. And we both feel a little kinder towards Texan Gal 1. Must have been a terrible time for that little girl and her family.

I feel a need to show Texan Gal 1 some support, now that I know the story. I take one of the wet wipes from my bag, the wipes that we keep to clean our bums with in dodgy public toilets, lean across the aisle and say, "Tell her to put this on her forehead. It will cool her head."

Texan Gal 2 smiles gratefully and places the wet wipe above her friend's face mask. And there she sits, in the middle of Egypt, surrounded by some of the great wonders of the world, oblivious to them all, with her face covered by a paper mask and a bum wipe, her eyes closed against the pain, looking for all the world like an Egyptian mummy. Which perhaps is appropriate after all.

We are on our way again. The Temple of Queen Hatshepsut is next.

Now, Hatshepsut is a word that seems to get most people's tongues in a tangle. Even trying to spell it correctly gets me in a tangle. Our group variously calls her Hatshetsup, Hapshepsot, Hashtepsot, Pashsetot, Hapshetshit and Hashsouppot. Hubby and I decide to simplify things and call her Hattie.

But Mr and Mr Gay Couple have their own pet name for her. The First Gay Cross-dressing Queen in History. She wasn't the only female Pharaoh, there had been others, including one called Sobekneferu (trying saying that after a few drinks!), but they ruled as women. Not Hattie. She took on the mantle of a man and lived accordingly. Mr and Mr Gay Couple seem to know more about her than the tour guide, recounting to us stories of how she dressed as a man, stuck a fake beard on her face, rode to war with her troops, had a baby dressed as a man, had sex with men and women, and generally stuck it to the powerful males of her day. After she died, her successors tried to erase her from history by destroying and defacing anything to do with her. But here she is in the 21st century, recognised and lauded as a powerful Pharaoh of Egypt for over twenty years. Mr and Mr Gay Couple feel a sense of personal pride in her. An LGBT hero way before the title was even coined.

I admire her because she stuck it to the blokes. Go Hattie!

It's an uphill walk to her Temple and our legs are still like jelly, but we get there and stroll around, consulting our brochures about what we are looking at, admiring the statues and hieroglyphics, as well as the fact that Egyptian Pharaohs had no problems with self esteem. Even when they were little, old and frail, as we had noted from the many well preserved mummies in the Cairo Museum, they depicted themselves on their temples as tall, beautiful, broad shouldered, narrow hipped, strong and perfect in every way. In fact, after seeing all the temples, we begin to think the same artist was used in each one, as we keep seeing the same face and body, even though the subjects lived thousands of years apart from each other. Only one Pharaoh appears to be depicted differently. Akhenaton was

205

depicted more realistically with his skinny torso, big belly and long face and skull. Not to mention his singular ways. And he scored the great beauty of his time, Nefertiti. Hubby and I think he wouldn't do so well today on Tinder. He's definitely a Swipe Lefter. If you are over 50, you probably don't know what that is. It's an online dating site that brings up a picture of someone. If you like them, you swipe right. If you don't, you swipe left. Takes a nano-second to decide. The only reason we know is because we have teenage grandchildren. I think Tinder is brutal. They think it is convenient. Different times.

Back to Hattie. Mr and Mr Gay Couple ask us to take numerous photos of them together in their idol's Temple and we are happy to comply. We see Mr and Mrs Teetering Heels leaning against a statue in the shade, looking a tad bored. Her feet look swollen in her sensible flat sandals. Mr and Mrs Red Pants are strolling hand in hand, just delighted to be both here and lucid at the same time. Mr and Mrs Intelligentsia are discussing false beards with Mr and Mrs Effusive, we aren't sure why, and Mr and Mrs Gentle Wit are sitting on a step, sipping from their drink bottles. The Two Oldies are standing before a statue with awestruck faces, while Ms Miseryguts waxes lyrical about how there should be seating provided for old people like them. The Two Oldies pretend not to hear her and move away. Mrs Love-a-Chat is telling Miss Well Travelled a story about a dead goldfish, while Miss Well Travelled is telling Ms Fat 'n Loud about her cholesterol levels. Miss Fat 'n Loud looks over both their heads and grins at us. She is a real trouper.

We finish wandering around the Temple, it's actually smaller than it looks from a distance, and start walking back to the bus park. And we come to the Tourist Trap. Several sites we visit in Egypt have a different entrance to the exit. You go into the site through a gate or a series of steps - so many steps in Egypt, they love putting their monuments high up - and exit a different way that passes through the inevitable market alley, lined with vendors selling all the usual stuff. There is no other way out. And there we find our 3 Shopping Sisters. They didn't spend much time at the Temple, instead opting for the lure of the market stalls. They have filled several mesh bags that they carry at all times at the bottom on their handbags. I can see their purchases through the mesh - scarfs, tops and trousers, jewelled sandals, pointy-toed slippers, jewellery, leather wallets and knock-off handbags. I had asked them that morning at breakfast how they fitted all their shopping into their suitcases. They grinned at me. They had it all worked out before they left home. At each hotel, they would parcel up their purchases and send them home. Then they had the excitement of unpacking them all and rediscovering what they had bought when they got back home. Cost an arm and a leg, but they had factored that into their budget. So shop away, girls!

I hear Ms Miseryguts cry out behind me and turn to look. She is cowering, holding her handbag before her like a shield as a couple of young vendors badger her to buy their wares. She is genuinely frightened by these harmless youths who are only trying to make an honest living off the prosperous western tourists. Miss Well Travelled comes up behind her and says, "Oh don't be such a girl's blouse. Just keep walking!" She strides on with the confidence of experience, saying, "Shoo!" to a couple of insistent vendors, who quickly choose another target, for why waste time on someone who is not interested in buying anything? That is simply not good business. Ms Miseryguts quickly steps into Miss Well Travelled's wake and hurries after her.

We pass a stall and I spy a necklace and matching earrings on the wall that reminds me of something I saw in Tutankhamun's display at the Cairo Museum. I step toward it. Hubby says, "Come on, you don't need another necklace." Of course, I ignore him. He knew I would. He doesn't really mind and dutifully waits while I look at the necklace. The vendor is onto me in a flash. "Very good price for madam. Only 10 Egyptian pounds." I know very well it is not worth that, but I think it is pretty and decide to play the game. It is, after all, what every stall vendor expects of us tourists.

"1 Egyptian pound."

"Oh no madam, it is finest quality. 10 Egyptian pounds."

"1."

"9 Egyptian pounds."

"1."

"8."

"1."

"7."

"1."

"6."

"1."

"5." He suddenly looks a little smug. This must be his usual winning bid. I am a little irritated by his smugness.

"1."

"4." He is looking a bit uncertain.

"1."

"3." He is not looking so smug now.

I look at the necklace again and decide I don't really want it. After all, I've got a drawer full of such travel jewellery at home. I start to walk away. He is calling after me, "3 Egyptian pounds! Very cheap!"

I keep walking. I as far as I am concerned, the game is over. We are a good ten metres away when I hear him call out, "Very well, madam, 1 Egyptian pound!"

I am surprised that he agreed to my offer and we walk back to the stall. Hubby gives me a gentle nudge of approval as I hand the pound coin over. The vendor takes the necklace and earrings off the wall and turns away to wrap them in a bit of tissue paper. He bends over it as Hubby whispers to me, "You are now an honorary Scotsman." The vendor hands us the package and we continue on our way.

We are back on the bus and on our way to Karnak when I decide to open the package and inspect my latest purchase. And discover that the very canny little vendor had the last word. When he turned away to wrap the jewellery, he had deftly removed the catch from the necklace and the two hooks from the earrings. They were unwearable! I showed Hubby and we laughed. When we get back home, I visit a nearby craft shop, buy a new catch and two earring hooks for a dollar and make them wearable. And every time I wear them, I remember that little chap and how smug he must have felt when we walked away thinking we had won. Happy, funny memories.

It's about now that we begin to experience the Templed-Out syndrome. There was a movie made in 1969 called "If it's Tuesday, this must be Belgium" about the phenomena of package tours. We know all about that experience from our own package tour experiences - racing from place to place, trying to fit as much in as possible because we know that we will never pass that way again, taking too many photographs and hoping we remember what they are when we get home, boring our families and friends with stories of our travels whilst contradicting each other constantly. "It rained all day when we were in that garden in Italy." "No, that was in France." "It was in Italy. I remember because the garden was so steep." "No, the garden in Italy was by the sea. The one that was so steep was in France." "No, it was in France, I remember because we had to stop in a little cafe for lunch and the waiter was from Australia." "That cafe was in Spain." So we get the photos out and argue over them while our guests develop headaches and suddenly remember early starts the next day and have to leave, and after they've gone, we find the photographs of the right garden in the right country when it rained all day. It was in Switzerland, by a lake, and the waiter at the cafe was Irish. Oh well, close enough.

In Italy, we heard the expression, "troppa arte" - "too much art". You see so many paintings and ceiling murals, so many churches and cathedrals that you become Arted-Out. Troppa Arte.

In Egypt, you become Templed-Out. You can't remember what temple was where and what it had in it. They all begin to merge into another pile of rocks. Even when you pour over the photos back home, you need to Google the temples and monuments by name to match them to the photos, unless you have a clever camera with a GPS that tells you where each photo was taken. That wasn't around in 2010, so when I get home, I begin to look through my 3,000 plus photos with the intention of keeping only the best of them and making up an album, but never actually get around to doing it. We still have them on a USB stick. Might have a crack at watching them on our new state of the art TV soon, with our iPads on our laps so that we can check what temple we are looking at, and put the best of them into an album. Or not.

So we are feeling a little under-excited by our next temple visit. Even though it's a goodie.

As we leave our bus at Karnak, Mohamed points out the public loos. Now, lets get something clear here. Toilets are critically important to Old Farts. Old Fart males make the joke about "never pass a toilet, never trust a fart, and never waste an erection." Old Fart females would modify that a little to "never pass a toilet, never trust a cough or sneeze, and never pass a sale." So we all make our way to the toilets before beginning our tour of Karnak.

Have you ever found two toilets exactly alike when you travel? I haven't. I am staggered at the myriad ways toilets are designed and maintained, from the basic stinking holes in the ground of roadside stops to the glamorous marbled affairs of upmarket hotels. The variation can be found in almost every country. We had grown accustomed to seeing the hole in the ground next to seated loos in Egypt, as it is a country that is very accommodating to it's many foreign tourists. We had also grown accustomed to seeing the toilet-paper-boys standing outside every public toilet we stopped at. You need to pay them for toilet paper. 1 Egyptian pound was the usual fee. The boys were often quite young, anything from ten to fifteen, standing there with a roll of loo paper in their hand, taking the money and letting you tear off a few sheets before you go in. Some of the boys actually stand inside the ladies' loo with their toilet rolls, which was a bit unnerving at first, as gender segregation is so expected in the western world, but we got used to that as well. They aren't interested in listening to a lot of old ladies weeing, they are only interested in

213

their pound coins. It's not the most pleasant way to make a living.

But here in Karnak, we experience another version of the public loo. It is unisex, something that Old Farts do not like at all. There is a row of cubicles with low doors high off the ground, so you can see the heads and feet of people sitting down, not to mention squatting bums of those using the holes in the ground, and a row of urinals for the men right next to the cubicles. It is quite old, smelly and not so clean, but we know that thousands of people use it and what else can you expect under the circumstances. We Old Fart women have developed a technique of perching ourselves one inch above a toilet seat, so that skin contact is never made. And we wouldn't even attempt to squat over a hole in the ground. Getting down is hard enough, but getting up is impossible.

So we are all lined up outside this loo, men and women, and the toilet-paper-boy is doing a roaring trade. I'm not too worried about him because I carry tissues and wet wipes in my bag for just such occasions, but I will still give him his pound coin because he has to make a living, and it's respectful. But not everyone in our group feels that way, especially when I see that he is only handing out one little square of paper to each customer. One square! No woman can manage with that. Four is the absolute minimum. And if it's more than a wee, well you need a good deal more. I look at the pleasant face of the toilet-paper-boy and I just know he hasn't a clue what women need to clean themselves up. But most of us are prepared with our own supplies.

Not so Ms Miseryguts. She is in front of me. She hands over her coin, he hands her a little square, and she shakes her head. "No, that's not enough." She holds her hand out for more. So does he. She needs to pay him more. She's not happy with that. "No, just give me more," she demands in her whiney voice. He clutches the precious toilet roll to his chest and keeps holding his hand out. And she breaks an Old Fart tourist rule. She is disrespectful and rude to a local. She grunts with disgust and grabs the toilet roll out of the boy's hand. He looks shocked as she pulls reams of paper off the roll and roughly pushes it back into his hand. Then she storms into a cubicle, muttering her displeasure as she seems to do without end about everything.

I am mortified. She has insulted this poor boy who is only doing his job as instructed by his boss. He has been polite, she has not. This is not like the bargaining game with the stall vendor where both parties know the original asking price is never the expected final payment. This is a straight out business arrangement and Ms Miseryguts should be used to it by now. I am ashamed of my colleagues' behaviour. I feel terribly sorry for the boy and fish some extra pound coins out of my bag. Seven to be exact. I offer them to him and say, with as kind a smile as possible, "May I please have some extra?" He counts seven squares, tearing each one off individually. Hubby behind me does not need any. Men don't when they take a leak. But he sees what I am doing and hands five coins to the boy. We are trying to make it up to him. Somehow, it seems important that he thinks well of us.

We have paid more for toilet paper than we paid for the necklace and earrings. Oh well.

I go into a cubicle and hold my breath. It is pretty foul. I keep my head down and pretend no one can see over the door or under the door, or hear me tinkling or see me wiping my bum. We are all in the same boat. I get it over with as quickly as possible and leave the cubicle to wash my hands, only to discover that there is no water coming out of the tap.

I see Mr and Mrs Red Pants in a cubicle together, the dog lead firmly in place as they take turns, one standing, one sitting.

Ms Miseryguts is still in a cubicle and peering anxiously over the top of the door while she grapples with the miles of toilet paper she helped herself to.

216

Mrs Twinkling Eyes is conducting herself inside her cubicle as if she is at a photo shoot, smiling as she perches elegantly above the stained seat and even winking at her husband as he leaves the urinal.

Little Mrs Teetering Heels is the only one short enough to disappear behind a cubicle door, but I can hear her groaning as she lowers and holds herself in place with a degree of pain and effort.

The 2 Texan Gals go into a cubicle together and one stands with her back to the little door while the other sits, effectively shielding the tinkler. Not a bad strategy. I should have suggested it to Hubby, although I expect he wouldn't have been too keen.

The 3 Shopping Gals are taking turns, with two standing guard outside while the other perches.

Ms Fat 'n Loud is struggling, as the cubicles are quite small and she is not. She manoeuvres carefully so as not to make contact with the dirty walls, door or seat. There is nothing she, or any of us, can do about the faeces spattered, urine dribbled floor. We'll have scoured the wee and poo off our shoes with desert sand before we've gone too far.

Miss Well Travelled is assisting The Two Oldies, bless her, even leaning over the door to offer a stabilising hand while the highly embarrassed ladies make the best of it.

Miss Know-it-all, who has something to say about everything, appears to have met her match here, for she is speechless, and it is another minute before I realise she is holding her breath while she hurries her wee along and gets out as fast as she can.

Mr and Mr Gay Couple are sharing a urinal, their shoulders touching as they shake their willies before putting them back in their trousers.

Mr and Mrs Intelligentsia have both pursed their lips and wrinkled their noses as they wordlessly let us all know that this is all beneath them.

Mr and Mrs Effusive are tackling it all head on in their usual practical way and are the first to finish.

Mr Gentle Wit looks over his shoulder whilst at the urinal to make sure that his wife is alright. Like me, she is keeping her head down and getting it over with.

That leaves Mrs Love-a-Chat, who has somehow made a link between this hellish public toilet and the birth of her first child. Something about mess and smell and being slippery and how she needed forceps and her husband couldn't get away from work to attend the birth, but that was fine because he didn't like her screaming anyway and she tried to be quiet with the others. Or something like that. Oh well, I suppose she understands what she is talking about. I sure don't.

We exit as quickly as we can, for another tour group is lining up to do their deals with the toilet-paper-boy. Hubby and I wipe our hands vigorously with the antiseptic hand wash he carries in his backpack and walk back to our group's meeting point. He leans towards me and whispers, "Did you get all that?"

"Yep."

"I didn't see you take any notes."

"Don't worry, it's all committed to memory."

He grins. "Glad I didn't need a number two."

I concur.

We ignore Ms Miseryguts behind us as she complains loudly about the terrible way tourists are treated in Egypt and how dirty everything is. Tourists are treated very well in Egypt and it's only sand. And a little poo occasionally. I've seen more mess in a nappy after a poosplosion with a breastfed baby. It all washes off. Perhaps she is less comfortable around such things because she hasn't had children. Everyone has their reasons for being the way they are. But I think it is a pity that she seems oblivious to the magnificence around us, and the unimportance of a rather grubby public loo. I wonder is she complains about her gorgeous marbled bathroom at the hotel as well. Of course she does. She informs us later that day that marble is slippery and dangerous when it's wet, and the hotel should know better. There is always something. Thank goodness we only have one like her on our trip. We've had more in the past. Ah well, live and let live. You get better - or worse - at that as you get older.

Our group gathers around Mohamed and he starts to tell us about the Avenue of Sphinxes we are about to walk past before entering the Temple. And then we hear a familiar voice nearby. "Hey, check it out! Ride 'em cowboy!"

It is the young man from the Australian bus tour we had encountered a few days ago. We all turn as one to see him and several other lads climbing onto the sphinxes and sitting astride them as they would horses. One cries out, "Yeehaa!" and they proceed to behave badly to the encouragement of the rest of their group. But not their tour guide. What his charges are doing is totally wrong and he berates them loudly.

And then Mr Red Pants hollers, "Yeehaa!" and we see him dragging Mrs Red Pants along as he makes his way toward one of the Sphinxes. Oh gawd, he's going to join the urban cowboys. Mohamed is onto him like a shot and pulls him back gently. Hubby and Mr Effusive move fast, each take an arm and try to steer him away. But he is single minded. "Ride the horsey!" he cries.

And then Ms Fat 'n Loud steps forward, puts her hands on his shoulders and forcibly turns him away, all the time saying, "There's a better horsey in the bus. Come, let's go see the other horsey."

Mr Red Pants grins and allows himself to be led away. Miss Well Travelled says to Mrs Red Pants, "I'll sit on the bus with you. I've been here before. I don't need to see it again." She nods to Ms Fat 'n Loud. "You go see Karnak. You don't want to miss it. It really is something."

Mr Red Pants is led away and quickly settled on the bus. Mrs Red Pants has some help and we are all grateful to Miss Well Travelled for that.

Ms Fat 'n Loud stays with the rest of us as Mohamed leads us past our cringeworthy young countrymen, who are by now off the sphinxes and looking very chastened indeed, especially as two policemen with the ever present bloody big guns have moved closer to their group and seem to be watching them carefully. We, the well behaved invisible Old Farts, slide quietly past.

As we pass through the entrance to the actual temple, I am nearly knocked off my feet by a group of tourists in a terrible hurry. They are young Chinese and seem oblivious to our presence. They push past us and keep moving, their cameras and phones held above their heads as they snap away at everything in every direction, without stopping long enough to take it all in. They continue to push their way through the many groups in front of us, all the time keeping their eyes on their cameras and phones. They are missing the experience of actually being here completely. Hubby and I look at each other and shake our heads.

Mohamed gives us the usual spiel and then lets us wander about for a while. Hubby and I lean against the shady side of one of the magnificent carved pillars and I can feel the history all around me. We snap a few photos, then continue on. We catch up with the hasty Chinese and observe them standing in a huddle, now with their heads down as they Facebook and Tweet their photos, or whatever the Chinese equivalent of Facebook and Twitter is. Again, they are not looking around them.

Hubby says, "Is it just us? Are we the ones doing it wrong? Are we dinosaurs?"

I say, "Viva la dinosaur," and we have a quiet chuckle.

Hubby checks his watch, says, "Rendezvous time," and we head back to our appointed meeting place with Mohamed.

Back on the bus, we find Mr Red Pants staring out of the window, his eyes empty, his wife exhausted. Miss Well Travelled whispers to us, "She gave him a sedative. He'll be OK now." Our collective hearts go out to both of them.

We stop at a papyrus factory, not expecting it to be much after such an amazing day. And we are all feeling a little tired by now. But we are in for a surprise.

A young man tells us how papyrus is made and introduces us to some of the papyrus artists. Their work is on display on several large tables and we stroll around, trying to decide whether we want to buy something, what we should get and whether or not it will go through Customs. Australia has strict laws about things like that. We are assured that each item comes with a certificate guaranteeing its health and safety. And I spy a painted papyrus that I instantly fall in love with and absolutely have to have. It is rolled up and prepared for me.

I turn to see how our group are getting on. Standing behind me are the 3 Shopping Sisters, their arms filled with as many papyrus paintings as they can hold. Shopping Sister 1 grins at me. "They don't weigh much, we can take them home in our suitcases."

Shopping Sister 2 says, "That means we can buy lots. We've got lots of relatives and friends to buy presents for."

Shopping Sister 3 says, "They're not getting any of mine! I like them all."

Sister 1. "What are you going to do with them?"

Sister 3. "Frame them and hang them, of course."

Sister 2. "Where will you hang them? You're place isn't that big."

Sister 3. "The shed."

Sister 1. "Your husband's shed?"

Sister 3. "Yessiree."

Sister 2. "He'll never let you. That's his space."

An evil glint appears in Sister 3's eyes. "It was. He's going away for two weeks in August. His annual fishing trip with his buddies."

Sisters 1 and 2 gasp. "You wouldn't!" "That's grounds for divorce!"

Sister 3. "He's too old, too fat and too lazy to divorce me. All he does in there is drink. He can drink in the living room. That shed is mine."

Sister 1. "He'll fight you."

Sister 3. "Not if I pay for Foxtel in the living room."

Sister 2 grins. "You always were the clever one."

And that is that. Hubby grimaces as we turn away. A fellow shed-male has been ousted from the sacred domain. I silently cheer. There's a gal who knows all a man needs is Fox Sport and a beer and he doesn't care where he is. You go girl!

When I get home, I have our beautiful papyrus painting elegantly framed and hung in the lounge room. And every time I look at it, I imagine Shopping Sister 3's husband slumped in front of his favourite sport program with his third or fourth beer while his wife straightens her many papyrus paintings in the shed.

224

We fly back to Cairo, looking forward to a couple of days in that amazing city before we leave this particular tour to join another in Europe. We are booked into the same hotel we'd stayed in at the beginning of our tour. Hubby and I freshen up, but don't change as we are quite exhausted, and we decide to have dinner outside in the beautiful hotel gardens where a silver service barbecue is offered. It is a perfect evening and the gardens are softly lit, making it seem a magical place. It was used for the filming of Death On The Nile, with David Suchet as the famous Hercule Poirot. It all looks very familiar, as I've seen that particular Agatha Christie at least six times. A bit of a fan of the old David Suchet Poirot. As are several others on our tour, for they are also wandering around, finding the very same trees and garden beds we remember from the movie. I imagine the old king wandered around these gardens in whatever form they took back then, on an evening such as this, just as we are doing.

We spy Mrs Teetering Heels ordering her barbecue dinner. I try not to gasp. She isn't doing casual and comfy as we are doing. No, she has squeezed herself into a tiny black cocktail dress, no stockings, no shapewear, and strappy skyscraper-heel sandals covered in sparkly diamante. Mr

Teetering Heels is keeping her upright, but it is a perilous task. She has also teased her hair into a bouffant that reminds me of the 1960s, and applied so much makeup that her eyes in her small chubby face look like two black holes in the snow with a fatal red gash below. And the lighting isn't helping. People are staring at her. And not politely.

Hubby and I find a small table, our drink order is taken and Hubby goes to get our barbecue. We are so tired that we don't feel like socialising. We just want to eat and go to bed. But here come Mr and Mrs Teetering Heels. I don't think they planned to sit with us, but we are the first table they pass and Mrs Teetering Heels simply cannot go any further. She looks at me pleadingly and I indicate Hubby's chair. She almost falls into it. Poor darling. Why is she doing this to herself? Mr Teetering Heels brings two more chairs to our little table and puts their laden plates on it. Then Hubby comes back with our plates and it's like fitting puzzle pieces together to get everyone's dinner on the same table.

And then she says in her soft, squeaky voice, "I thought it was a cocktail party tonight."

I say, "No, that's tomorrow night."

"Oh. I'll have to wash this dress. I only brought one cocktail dress."

"You could always wear something else."

"Oh, no, I brought specific outfits for each occasion. It has to be this dress for the cocktail party."

"It wouldn't matter..."

"No. It has to be this dress. I mean, you have to get it right, don't you?"

Our husbands have their heads down, trying to keep their food from falling off the table and also trying not to get involved in the conversation.

I say, "I don't think anyone would notice..."

"Oh, they would. I mean, everyone is so...so... proper the way they dress. You know what I mean? The right top with the right bottom with the right accessories. And the shoes. They all do it so easily. And everyone is so...tall. You have to keep up, don't you?" She shovels food into her mouth and looks around her uncertainly. And I get it. She is so insecure around other women that she is never sure whether she gets it right or not. Well, she isn't the first woman to feel insecure around more attractive, better dressed women. I've been in rooms where every other woman, without exception, has been more attractive and better dressed than me and, despite being very comfortable in my own skin, I have wished I'd worn something different or done more with my hair. It has never affected me or changed my personal habits to the extent that it obviously affects Mrs Teetering Heels, probably because I am more interested in what I think of others than what they think of me. One of the foibles of being a writer perhaps?

I am feeling her insecurity tangibly and want to say something encouraging, but I am pipped at the post by a simple and poignant gesture. Mr Teetering Heels puts his fork down and places his hand over hers. He says quietly, "You always look lovely, dear."

Mrs Teetering Heels shoots him a tender look and smiles. And I can see that this is a genuine love match, an enviable partnership and a harmonious one. They are a lovely couple and I am deeply touched.

I say, "We're doing the markets tomorrow. Perhaps you'll find something there for tomorrow night."

"Oh, I'm not going to that. We're having a rest day tomorrow." I hear a satisfied grunt from Mr Teetering Heels and I'm not sure if it's for the food or the day off tomorrow.

"That's a pity. They sound like fun."

"My husband says if I put one more thing in the suitcases, he'll rupture a disc."

"Suitcases? How many do you have?"

"I have two. Two large suitcases. He has one small one. We have to pay for excess baggage on our flights, but I don't mind."

I had wondered how she managed to have a completely different outfit every day, sometimes twice a day, with shoes and bag to match each outfit. So far, she has worn more clothes than I have in my entire wardrobe, and her shoe collection must fill one of those large suitcases on their own.

"Do you always travel like that?"

"This is our first trip."

Mr Teetering Heels mumbles into his food, "And our last." I pretend I haven't heard him.

I want to change the subject and say, "Well, we've travelled before. And we're going on to a couple of tours in Europe after leaving Cairo. We'll be celebrating our sixth wedding anniversary in Paris."

Mrs Teetering Heels' face lights up. "We'll be celebrating our seventeenth wedding anniversary next month! So you met later in life, too?"

I nod and tell her how old Hubby and I were when we met. And she tells me how old she and her much younger husband were when they met and married. I mentally add on seventeen years and nearly gag on my food. She is almost 80! The same age as Young Oldie. And my admiration for this woman skyrockets. What a trouper! Staggering around in her ridiculous shoes meant for much younger feet and backs, wearing her age-inappropriate little skirts and tops, and keeping up on this trip with us youngsters in our 60's - she's a star! An insecure star maybe, but a very determined and rather fearless one. I ask her if she'd like to share a bottle of champagne with us and she grins with delight.

DAY 9

CAIRO MARKETS

The following morning, our little group is feeling a bit slow. We rock up for breakfast late and consume many cups of good coffee. The only ones missing are Mr and Mrs Red Pants. Apparently, he did not have a good night and a doctor was called. They are resting in their rooms today.

This is a devoted shopping day which all of our menfolk, without exception, are moaning about, but which the rest of us are looking forward to. Even Ms Miseryguts is anticipating the day. She wants to stock up with presents for her relatives back home. Mr and Mr Gay Couple are planning to redecorate their New York apartment with whatever they buy today. They mean business. I'm open minded. I don't need anything. But what has that ever had to do with shopping on a trip away from home?

Most of us are dressed in casual linens, cottons and good walking sandals, but dear Mrs Teetering Heels is wearing her day-off clothes - a pair of sadly see-through white stretch leggings, a pink top with feathers hanging off it in odd places and teetering silver sandals. I can see her granny knicker VPL through the leggings. Definitely not shopping clothes. Mr Teetering Heels is wearing baggy shorts and rubber thongs. He ain't going nowhere today.

And then, to our surprise, Mr Socially Superior walks into the dining room. We had not expected to see him again. He is greeted warmly and we gather around him to ask after his wife.

"She's alright," he says, "but she won't come out of our room. Says she's going to stay there until we fly out in three days."

I say, "She's still not well?"

"No, she's good. The doctor's said she was fine to join the tour again. She's just a bit...washed out."

"She's not up to joining us today?"

"No, says she's got nothing to wear."

I do a double take. That doesn't sound like Mrs Socially Superior. I thought she travelled with more luggage than Mrs Teetering Heels.

Mrs Twinkling Eyes says, "She doesn't need to dress up. We aren't."

"No, she won't get out of her pyjamas."

Ms Fat 'n Loud shakes her head. "Don't like the sound of that. I think I'll look in on her before we go."

"She won't like that..."

Ms Fat 'n Loud has not revised her opinion of Mr Socially Superior and ignores him. "Anyone coming with me?" She looks meaningfully at me, Mrs Effusive and Mrs Twinkling Eyes. We all follow her to the lift.

When we come to the right room, Ms Fat 'n Loud knocks on the door. A weak voice inside says, "Who is it?"

"It's me, dear."

"I'm in bed. Can you come later?"

"No. Open the door." Well, that was blunt.

We hear shuffling about inside the room and the door opens.

Mrs Socially Superior looks like she has been through the grinding mill and then some. Her face is blotchy and peeling from the terrible sunburn, a large cold sore on her lip is weeping, her eyes are red, her hair is limp and her expression is sad enough to make me want to cry. Her baggy Kmart pyjamas (I have the same pair) and fluffy slippers make her unrecognisable from the overblown woman we knew before. She sees the four of us and flinches, moving to shut the door, but Ms Fat 'n Loud is in the room before she can do it. "Don't worry, dear, we're not here to bother you. We just want to see if we can do anything for you."

"No, I'm alright." The words are barely whispered.

Mrs Twinkling Eyes says gently, "I think not."

Mrs Effusive says cheerfully, "It's good to see you back."

I say, "We missed you."

The red eyes open a little. "You did?"

"Sure. We thought you'd want to come with us today. It's just the markets. All you have to do is stroll around. Your husband can carry the parcels..."

Mrs Socially Superior's face hardens a little. "Him? Carry my parcels? That'll be the day!"

There is an uncertain pause, then Ms Fat 'n Loud continues. "Well, you can't let him spoil your day. Come on, throw on some glad rags and we'll carry your shopping bags for you ourselves. You've missed enough already."

We all chime in. "Yes, we'll help you." "We'll stay with you." "We'll look after you."

Mrs Socially Superior is overwhelmed. She is obviously not used to this sort of support. "But look at me. I can't go like this. My face is a mess."

Mrs Twinkling Eyes gives her a professional ex-model once over. "Nothing a little moisturiser, some sunscreen and some clever makeup can't deal with."

"But my clothes. They make my skin red and sore. And my hair. Look at it. I'm a disaster!"

Ms Fat 'n Loud puts a heavy, reassuring hand on Mrs Socially Superior's shoulder. "No, you're not, dear. Your husband is, but you are not. And your clothes can be replaced." She pauses. "I expect it's the polyester that is irritating your skin. It's so sensitive after that heat stroke. Have you got anything that isn't polyester in your suitcase?"

Mrs Socially Superior ponders that. "No."

"You haven't got any linen or cotton at all?"

"I don't wear linen or cotton because I hate ironing."

Mrs Effusive says, "Oh my dear, where I come from, if you wear polyester, you die. No one wears synthetics in Darwin, I can tell you that now. It's just too bloody hot all year around. And you don't need to iron linen. If you dry it on a hanger, it's fine. I've got a nice white linen top that should fit you."

"But you are tiny. Nothing of yours would fit me."

"It's a wrap-around. It'll fit you. I'll go get it." She leaves.

Ms Fat 'n Loud says, "I've got some green elastic-waisted cotton trousers that should do the trick. They're nice and loose."

"Loose? No. Loose makes me look fat."

Ms Fat 'n Loud sighs. She is so over hearing this sort of thing. "You are fat, dear. So am I. Am I bothered? Life's for the living and being fat shouldn't stop you, so get over yourself and live with it. I'm getting you the green trousers." She leaves.

Mrs Twinkling Eyes says, "I'll get my makeup bag. I'll be back in a moment." She leaves.

I'm left facing Mrs Socially Superior. I say, "I can do your hair for you. Do you have a straightening iron?"

"Yes, but it's only one of those little travel ones. I don't know how good it is."

"I use one of them all the time."

Mrs Socially Superior eyes my plain grey hair distastefully. "Do you ever use it?"

I don't take the put down personally. "Not today. It's hat hair today, so it's a waste of time. But I can touch yours up if you like."

She is discomfited by all this friendly attention. "I don't know. They told me in the hospital not to use hairspray for a few weeks while my face settles down. How can I do my hair without hairspray?"

"Well, why don't we give it a try and see how it looks."

She submits, albeit not particularly gracefully.

The others return. Ms Fat 'n Loud has the lime green trousers as well as a pair of horrendous looking thick-soled leather sandals. Mrs Effusive is carrying a gorgeous linen top and a soft cotton scarf in jewel colours. Mrs Twinkling Eyes has brought her lovely blue straw hat as well as a large makeup bag. She holds up the weapons she is about to tackle Mrs Socially Superior with and I am impressed. I buy my makeup and moisturiser at the chemist shop back home, but these are top of the range cosmetics you need to go to a department store for. Guaranteed to impress Mrs Socially Superior, who closes her eyes uncertainly and submits to our ministrations.

We fuss over our embattled sister for about twenty minutes and when we stand back to survey her, it's an eat-your-heart-out-Trinny-and-Susannah moment. Mrs Socially Superior has been re-invented. And our thrown together combination of earthy sandals, wide green cotton trousers, white linen top and bright scarf work a treat. She is sporting a neat, shoulder length bob under the blue straw hat, her peeling skin has calmed down under the layer of moisturiser, and a touch of mascara and coral coloured lip gloss flatter her face much more than her usual heavy makeup. She turns to look at herself in the mirror and Ms Fat 'n Loud grabs her by the shoulders to prevent her. "No you don't," she says forcefully, "You look lovely. Take our word for it."

"Then why won't you let me..."

I say quickly, "How do you feel?"

Mrs Socially Superior moves around, touches her hair and face and says, "I feel OK. In fact, I feel...comfortable." She seems surprised. Obviously not a feeling she is used to.

Mrs Effusive says, "You look very pretty. We'd better go. The bus will be leaving shortly."

Mrs Twinkling Eyes says, "You look marvellous. Absolutely marvellous."

And somehow, a compliment from the ex model seems to work. Mrs Socially Superior lifts her head and says, "OK. Let's shop." She collects her handbag and we leave.

Our group has gathered together in the foyer to wait for our bus. As we approach, all eyes turn to look for Mrs Socially Superior. I am watching her husband. What will he think? And his reaction surprises me. He looks right through his wife. He doesn't recognise her! She opens her mouth, says, "I'm ready," and he nearly jumps out of his boots. And then she turns her back on him and joins us girls by the door.

He comes up behind her. "Alright, love?"

"Yes."

"Can I carry your bag for you?"

Mrs Socially Superior is stunned. She turns and stares at him. He tries to smile at her, and we see how shaky he is. So does she. She hands her bag to him and doesn't turn away again.

I breathe a silent sigh of relief. Goodness, we could have had fireworks there, but all looks well. I can only hope it continues.

The bus arrives and we launch into Cairo traffic. We have learned to trust our driver completely and are feeling quite relaxed as he wends his way through the madness. And then there is a lurch and a crunch and the bus stops. We have hit something. Oh gawd, I hope it isn't serious. Hubby and I look out the window and see a small red car skewed sideways into the side of the bus. The left hand front corner of the car is caved in. We can't see the damage to the bus.

Now, if this happened in Australia, other cars would stop to assist, the vehicles would be moved to the side of the road, the police would be called - especially if a bus with passengers was involved - and an ambulance sent for if there were injuries. If the accident was minor, both drivers would exchange registration and insurance details and possibly agree to deal with it themselves.

But this is Cairo. No other vehicles stop. In fact, they barely make any concession to the accident at all, moving past us without let up. Our bus driver calmly gets out of the bus as a young woman gets out of the red car. She seems unperturbed. Mohamed stays on the bus with us. He seems unperturbed as well. The bus driver examines the side of the bus, then pushes the little car away. The two drivers bend to look at the damage to the car and the bus, then nod to each other - and get back in their vehicles. She gets back in her little red car, starts the motor and continues on. Just like that. Smashed head light and all. No exchange of information, no apology or expression of regret. No assistance from any other road users around them. And when our bus driver boards, he grins back at us, sits in his seat and we join the mayhem again.

Only in Cairo.

Just before we get to our destination, Mohamed gives us a quick lecture about security and safety. Crossbody travel bags for the ladies and shirt front or jacket pockets for the men's wallets. While he is talking, I see the Two Oldies popping their purses into their bras. They will leave their bags on the bus. Smart move. Ms Fat 'n Loud is doing the same. I am wearing my crossbody travel bag which leaves both hands free to rifle through racks of clothes or tables of bargains. I've been shopping overseas before. Hubby has his travel pants on with the many hidden zipper compartments. He's good to go as well.

We arrive at the markets and disembark. This marketplace, Khan Al-Khalili, has been around for centuries and seen a lot of changes, but the old architecture has survived and it is a magical place. And it sure is exotic. No Kmart or Cheap as Chips feel here. It is a tsunami of glittering, luxurious, pretty, over the top gorgeously unnecessary things that make you want to buy everything in sight. Everything! Or so I think. I look at Hubby and he's already got that "get me outa here" look on his face.

We make our way past the shops and stalls. I want to stop and look at everything, but Hubby and I had agreed the night before that our main mission today will be to buy a rug for our family room. We had set a budget and that was what we are supposed to be looking for now. But I have a personal shopping budget of my own and I am saving that for after the rug hunt.

We find several rug shops and peruse them at Hubby's pace, which is not leisurely, but I had expected that. Men and women have very different speeds when shopping. Men go in with a list, get what they need and get out. Women, on the other hand, know how to peruse, to browse, to explore, to touch and feel every prospective purchase, to check one price against another, to try things on and stand before a mirror whilst deciding whether to commit or not, to remember what the price for the same item was three shops back, and of course, what they have at home that will go well with what they are buying today. So we look purposefully at many rugs of the appropriate size, colour and pattern and are delighted to find one that we both agree on. The transaction is agreed upon, arrangements are made to post the rug back home and we are done. It has only taken an hour and a half.

We need coffee!

We have heard about the very old and famous El Fishawy Coffee Shop and find it easily. It is divine! I could gush about this place for hours - the smell, the decor, the atmosphere, the coffee, the friendly staff, and the fact that we can actually sit down and stop for a little while. And one by one, our group wanders in and joins us. We find ourselves at a table next to Ms Miseryguts and Miss Well Travelled. Mr and Mrs Twinkling Eyes are nearby and Mr and Mrs Effusive right across from us.

And to our chagrin, all we can hear is Mr Miseryguts complaining. In this marvellous place, this marvellous moment, she has her head in her purse, pulling out coins and putting them in a row on the table and saying over and over, "They short changed me. They short changed me. They are robbers. They steal from me every chance they get. They are nothing but crooks!"

Well, Miss Well Travelled has had enough. She reaches out, puts her hand over Ms Miseryguts purse and says, "Tell me one thing you enjoyed today."

Ms Miseryguts looks up, startled. She doesn't understand the question. I feel emboldened. And probably a bit pissed off after over a week of listening to that whiny voice without let up. "She wants to hear something good about your day." Miss Well Travelled gives me a wink and we wait.

Well, poor Ms Miseryguts is quite lost for words. She looks at both of us and starts to say, "But he short changed..."

Miss Well Travelled jumps in. "No, he didn't. I saw what you gave him and how much you got back. But I don't want to hear about that. I want to hear something good about today. Come on, tell us."

Ms Miseryguts opens her mouth, closes it, opens it and her eyes glaze over a little. She really can't think of a thing.

Miss Well Travelled shakes her head and sighs. She calls a waiter over and orders more coffee. And she disengages from Ms Miseryguts. As do I. Life is too short.

Hubby grimaces at me as we bend over our coffees. He murmurs, "Poor bugger. All her travel stories will be about how she got shafted and ripped off."

We sip our coffee and are happy to be us.

Mohamed joins us and tells us he is taking the Two Oldies back to the hotel. They have had enough. Does anyone else want to go back? The rest of us can stay until the appointed time to leave.

I hold my breath.

And I am rewarded. Ms Miseryguts raises her hand and whines, "I want to go back. I feel safe at the hotel."

Miss Know-it-all and Mrs Love-a-Chat raise their hands. They are tired and would welcome an afternoon off. And then Texan Gal 1 raises her hand and waits for Texan Gal 2 to follow suit, but she doesn't. Instead, she says to Texan Gal 1, "You go back, dear, I'll stay on. And I'll bring you something nice. A surprise." She smiles and I can see her hopeful eyes as Texan Gal 1 thinks about it, and finally nods her assent.

Now Hubby is looking at me pleadingly. I say, "Sure, I'll be fine."

He looks relieved. "You'll stay with the others?"

"Of course."

"Do you need any money?"

I smile. "No. I've got enough."

Hubby gets up. Mr Twinkling Eyes says, "Are you going back to the hotel?"

"Yep. The missus approves."

Mr Effusive says, "Sounds like a plan to me."

And all the married men, with the exception of Mr and Mr Gay, have a few quick words with their wives and head back to the hotel with Mohamed. I know they will spend the rest of the day with beer and wine in hand and talk about golf and football and the exorbitant cost of travel. And I wonder if any of them will find it curious that not one of their wives argued with them when they suggested returning with Mohamed.

But do we care what they are talking about or thinking? No we do not. Because we are free. Free to shop!

And we do. We regroup outside Le Fishawy. The 3 Shopping Sisters saw a cushion shop earlier and have decided to replace every cushion in all three of their homes. Mrs Intelligentsia saw an antique book shop she wants to check out and Mrs Gentle Wit decides to go with her. Mr and Mr Gay Couple spy a shop with elaborate candlesticks and head there.

Mrs Socially Superior is looking a bit lost. And then Miss Well Travelled grabs her by the hand and says, "I know just the place for you." She looks at Ms Fat 'n Loud. "You'll like it, too. Everything is loose, cool and fabulous."

Well, that sounds irresistible to me, Mrs Effusive and Mrs Twinkling Eyes as well, and we follow Miss Well Travelled to a narrow doorway that gives nothing away. It's only when we go through that we realise we have entered a linen/cotton/silk Tardis paradise. Below high, ornate ceilings are row upon row of the most beautifully coloured, beaded and bejewelled garments and every one of them designed to skim in the most flattering way across the lumps and bumps of women of a certain age and shape. And no polyester in sight. Around the edge of the room are shelves jammed with shoes in every colour, style, heel height and degree of comfort, and all of them real leather. Scarves in more colours than the rainbow hang from the ceilings and the walls are adorned with thousands of baubles, bangles and beads. I'm the Jingle Jangle Bangle Lady with a weakness for anything that shines and glitters and I'm in Heaven!

The next two hours are a whirl and I come out with an empty purse and a full heart. Mrs Socially Superior has spent almost $5000 and declares that she will burn her entire wardrobe when she gets home. Once her new purchases have arrived, that is. Most of her purchases are being posted home.

We meet the 3 Shopping Sisters and Texan Gal 2 and tell them about our shopping bliss. They tell us where they have been. We go there and they go where we just came from. Another hour passes, seemingly in a flash, and it is time to gather at our point of departure. Mohamed is waiting for us.

He doesn't ask us how it went. He can see from our elevated state of excitement that it went very well indeed. As we settle on the bus, Mrs Socially Superior brags about how much she spent and we brag about how much we helped her spend it. And then Mr and Mr Gay Couple tell us how much they spent and we are speechless. I could build a three bedroom house on an acre with what they spent today.

As we pull out of the bus park, Mrs Socially Superior looks out of the window and says, to no one in particular, "$5000. Just on me. Put that in your pipe and smoke it, you tight arsed son of a...."

Every one of us knows who that is directed at, even though he isn't here on the bus. We say not a word.

The cocktail party that evening is a lively affair. It is held in the gardens, the waiters are plentiful, the platters they keep bringing around are sumptuous and we eat and drink ourselves silly. Mr and Mrs Red Pants are absent, but the word goes around that they plan to join us tomorrow for our farewell lunch. We hope so. Chairs are produced for the Two Oldies, but the rest of us stand in little groups, the women holding champagne glasses with our little fingers extended a tad pretentiously, the men with red wine or beer in hand and not a little finger to be seen.

Some of us women have dressed in our new purchases from the day's shopfest and we feel chic and attractive. It's amazing how a good shopfest lifts the spirits. Well, the spirits of the women, anyway. And the men are just happy that we are happy. Mrs Teetering Heels has washed out her tiny black cocktail dress and is wearing it tonight. And it looks like it has shrunk. Or she has expanded. Probably the latter if you consider what we've all been eating for the past week. But to our amazement, she has ditched her skyscraper heels and is wearing a pair of gaudy flat black sandals with so much coloured glass beading on them that she rattles when she moves. I consider that progress. As always, her hair is sprayed into impossible waves and her false eyelashes look so heavy that they make her look sleepy. But I feel proud of her. Those flat shoes are a real statement. And Mr Teetering Heels gets the night off. He's holding a cold beer instead of his wife's arm and looking very relaxed. Then we hear her say that her husband bought her new sandals from the hotel shoe shop as a present for her and aren't they pretty? He's a clever man.

Mrs Socially Superior is in particularly good form. She is wearing one of her new outfits - a loose jade coloured silk top with black jet beading over black silk harem pants and bejewelled leather sandals. She is still sporting her newly discovered simple, un-hairsprayed bob and wears only a little mascara and lipstick on her sun-blotched face. Her former killer nails are now short and polish free. Her new long earrings skim her shoulders and sparkle in the night lights. She is charming, funny and full of kind things to say about all present. Except for her husband. It's like he's invisible, despite his attempts at being nice to her. And my gut tells me there will be big changes for that couple when they get home. The dynamics of their relationship have changed forever. I hope they can work it out.

Mrs Love-a-Chat has cornered Ms Miseryguts and the 2 Texan Gals and is being duly ignored by them as she manages to turn the cocktail party into a story of how expensive disposable nappies are and why breastfeeding is better than bottle feeding. Ms Miseryguts has her head down and her hand in her purse. Still. She is muttering to herself about daylight robbery and writing to the tour company when she gets home to complain about the cost of everything. The 2 Texan Gals are getting into the champagne like there is no tomorrow and couldn't care less about the coin counting or anything to do with babies. Their eyes follow the waiters around and they grab everything they can as the platters come within reach.

Our 3 Shopping Sisters are talking cushions with Mr and Mr Gay Couple and having a vigorous debate about sequins versus hand embroidery. Mr and Mrs Intelligentsia are locked in discussion with Mr and Mrs Gentle Wit about which dictionary is the most relevant to the changing trends in the English language. Ms Know-it-all and Ms Fat 'n Loud are enthralled by Miss Well Travelled as she advises them on the best places for single women to travel alone.

As for Hubby and I, we spend the evening sharing travel stories with Mr and Mrs Twinkling Eyes and Mr and Mrs Effusive. We all know there are just so many more years we can be doing this sort of travel and so all travel stories are taken on board and carefully considered. Our next trip will be planned around a more relaxing schedule with fewer early mornings and less rushing around. Perhaps one of those luxury cruises down a river in Europe where you don't have to change hotels for two weeks and everything is done for you. Yep, sounds good to us.

It is a jolly evening. Hubby and I, usually in bed by 9.30pm, don't hit the pillow until after midnight. Tomorrow promises to be an easy day with a late-ish start, so it doesn't matter if we are a bit short of sleep.

It has been the best shopping experience of my life and one of those memories I revisit from time to time when I need something to make me smile. Those gals were great fun!

DAY 10

CAIRO MOSQUE AND THE
FAREWELL LUNCH

We wake late and realise we have less than an hour to get ourselves ready, have breakfast and board the bus. Hubby is a bit hungover after mixing his many drinks the night before and I feel bloated from so much overeating. We are both feeling less than sharp. Hubby runs through the shower in his usual manner, a bar of soap being all he needs. I feel sticky from the heat and humidity of the previous day and need all my usual shower stuff - moisturising body wash, loofah, razor, shampoo, conditioner, etc etbloodycetera. Hubby nags me to get a move on and I rush, only realising with horror as I dry myself that I have washed my hair under the shower in Nile water instead of over the wash basin with bottled water. Oh gawd. And I've been so careful up until now. My steel-gut Hubby says, "You'll be right. You didn't swallow any. Did you?"

Did I? I'm not sure. Oh well, I'll know soon enough.

Everyone is a little quiet at breakfast and there is lots of yawning going on. Mr and Mrs Red Pants are present. Well, in body at least. Mr Red Pants has that vacant look in his eyes and Mrs Red Pants does not leave his side. We all make a mental note to look out for them today.

Our last official tour today is to a mosque. It once belonged to a Sultan and it is stunning. Hubby and I wander around, taking our time and getting lots of photos. We both know we'll need to look at those photos when we get home as our heads are so foggy from the previous evening's imbibing that we aren't really connecting with the experience. And I wonder if that is why so many young tourists walk around holding their phones and cameras above their heads and taking photo after photo instead of looking around them. Are they hungover from late night revelries? I know they aren't in bed by 9.30 like us Old Farts. But then, you handle late night revelries so much better when you are young, don't you? You can party all night and still go to work the next day. Well, if memory serves me right. I seem to recall doing that a few times in the 60's and 70's. Back in the olden days, as our grandchildren say.

Hubby wanders off to find a loo and I linger near a doorway. We always choose a landmark to meet if we separate, it's a golden rule of travelling. It's a truly ghastly feeling to be in a foreign country and lose your tour group or your travelling partner and not know where you are. So we choose this lovely door and I stand patiently. The loos are outside, so Hubby will be awhile. The door opens behind me and I turn to look. About a dozen girls are coming through the doorway. They are all about 12 or 13 years old, all wearing brightly coloured hijabs, loose tops and trousers. Their hair is covered, but their faces are not. And their faces are gorgeous!

I smile at these beautiful young girls and they all smile back. The tallest of them says in perfect English, "Hello. Are you American or English?"

I say, "Oh no. Australian."

Every one of the girls grins widely and they gather around me. Being Australian obviously appeals to them.

One of the other girls says, "Sydney or Melbourne?"

Now, I need to explain something here before going on. Everywhere we have travelled overseas, people seem to think that all Australians live in Sydney, Melbourne or the Outback. And they've all seen Crocodile Dundee and The Adventures Of Priscilla: Queen Of The Desert and they believe they know everything about the Outback. When I tell people we live in Canberra, they look blank. When I then tell them Canberra is the Capital City of Australia, they still look blank. I once decided to say I lived in Melbourne when we were travelling through Greece. A Greek gentleman got very excited and said, "My cousin moved to Melbourne in 1956! Do you know him?" Only once has someone said, "Oh yes, Canberra's a lovely city," and he was a school teacher in Canada, so he knew a bit more than most. So being asked if we live in Sydney or Melbourne is what we are used to.

I look at the sweet face of the girl who has asked me the question and say, "Canberra. It is the Capital City of Australia."

Their faces light up. One of them says, "Oh, we did not know that. We will look it up when we get back to school."

I am impressed. They are bright girls. I ask, "What are you doing here today? It's a school day, isn't it?"

"We are having instruction. This," she points to the room where the girls have just come from, "is the girls' room, the boys are around the other side of the mosque."

"The mosque is beautiful." I grin back at them. "But you girls are more beautiful." They keep grinning. I can feel the love.

A sweet faced girl says, "What do you do in Australia?"

"I'm a writer."

"Oh, what do you write?"

"I write fiction for adults and children."

One of the girls takes her phone from a pocket and says, "What is your name?"

I tell them my pen name and she immediately does a search. She looks up with shock. "I found you!" She holds the phone out towards me and I can see she has found my website. "Is that you?"

"It is, but that photo is when I was still colouring my hair. I'm an Old Fart now and my hair is grey." I lift my hat and show them. They laugh and I laugh with them. Lordy lordy these girls are divine. I ask them, "What are your names?"

One by one, they tell me their names and the tallest girl catches my attention as she says, "My name is Alia."

"Oh, I have a granddaughter called Alia!"

The girls are delighted to hear that and Alia says, "Your granddaughter is Egyptian?"

"No. My daughter just loved the name."

And then Alia straightens, holds her head high and says, "My name is Alia and we are the daughters of pharaohs." All the girls lift their heads and nod. The Egyptians don't have a problem with self esteem. They know who they are. And I know I am experiencing one of those special moments when you actually connect with someone while you are travelling.

"I will tell my granddaughter that I have met you and how proud she should be of carrying the name Alia."

They all nod their approval. It seems I have said the exact right thing.

Alia says, "May we please take a photo of us with you?"

I am deeply honoured by this request and they gather around as each of them holds their phone up and takes a group selfie with me. We examine the selfies and declare them good. I ask them if I can take a video of them for my granddaughter and they giggle as they comply. I hold the camera before them, hit record and say, "Can you tell me your lovely names again?" One by one, they say their name and grin and giggle and it is delightful. Alia does her thing about being the daughters of pharaohs, I hit stop and thank them.

Hubby returns and the girls say hello. Then a man calls the girls and they are ushered away. As they go, they all turn to smile and wave at me and

I am brought to tears. I am tearing up writing this and remembering that unique moment.

I still have that selfie and that wonderful video. I look at it from time to time and hope all those beautiful young creatures are well and happy. And I wonder if any of them remember me.

Our group meets Mohamed at the appointed place and we are taken to a restaurant for our farewell lunch. After this lunch, our tour will be officially over. Some of us are leaving for the airport this afternoon, others tomorrow. Hubby and I are flying to Italy the next morning, so we are planning a relaxing afternoon of packing and napping. But first, the farewells.

We've been on package tours before and we know how it goes. There will be much laughter and good will, a little relief that being trapped in a confined space on a bus with strangers is over, promises of staying in touch and intentions of doing so. We also know that staying in touch rarely lasts. We will go home with everyone's email addresses and exchanged a few, "Hi, how are you?" emails and then it will gradually stop as we all realise that we have nothing in common outside of our trip, we don't know each other's family, friends or situation, we actually have nothing to talk about and our normal lives take over. There are exceptions to this occasionally, and indeed I have made a couple of friends I Facebook with and email from time to time, but the general rule is that it will peter out. But for now that doesn't matter, for the restaurant is wonderful, the company is good, the weather perfect and the food is fabulous.

The restaurant is silver service, a large terrace under canvas sails right next to the Nile River. Our tables are all next to the water and we have three hours to luxuriate here. After the entree is served, I go to the toilet feeling relaxed and happy. When I come out, I find chaos. Someone has gone missing!

I think at first it must be Mr Red Pants, but I see him attached to Mrs Red Pants by that leather dog lead, even while they eat. He's OK. No, it's Old Oldie. She was last seen going to the toilets when we first arrived and hasn't been sighted since. Mohamed is distraught. He has waiters looking in every nook and cranny of the restaurant. He checks the bus where the bus driver, who is watching TV on his iPad, reassures him that she hasn't tried to board the bus. The driver joins Mohamed in the search. This is a major concern for a tour company, not just for the welfare of the tourist, but because their reputation is at stake and there is always the question of insurance. If Old Oldie has met with some terrible fate, the tour company will be responsible. I am aware of these factors, but I see

259

quite clearly that Mohamed is genuinely worried about Old Oldie.

We have all left our tables and we wander around, looking over the terrace, scanning the river, checking the toilets for the umpteenth time. Hubby and I join a few others outside the restaurant and we agree to spread out. We all have Mohamed's mobile number. He reassures us he will text us all if she is found. We agree to do the same.

Young Oldie is standing by the restaurant entrance, leaning heavily on her walking stick. I say, "Are you alright, dear?"

She nods pensively. "She can't have gone far, you know. She's even slower than me."

Hubby says, "I hope she hasn't been harmed..."

Young Oldie smirks a little. "Oh, she'd bash anyone over the head with her walking stick if she felt threatened. She's a tough old bird." She looks around and says again, "She won't be far. And she won't have crossed the road on her own. She doesn't like Cairo traffic."

That gives us a clue. There are a couple of other restaurants nearby along the waterfront. Hubby and I go into the first one. No sign of her there. We wander into the second one, and there she is. Sitting alone at a little table next to the water, a Turkish coffee in her hand, staring out dreamily at the river. And totally unaware of the panic she has caused. Hubby says, "I'll let Mohamed know," and he gets his phone out of his pocket.

I go to her. She looks up and says sweetly, "Where have you all been? Have you all got Cairo Tummy?"

We can see our restaurant jutting out over the water nearby with our group looking frazzled on the terrace. I point them out. "We're over there."

She squints through her thick glasses. "Oh. What are you all doing there?"

"That's where we are meant to be."

She is confused. "Did we change venues?"

"No. We were always there."

"Oh." She thinks for a moment. "I thought it was a long way back from the toilets. Oh dear, did I make a wrong turn when I came out?"

"I think you may have."

Old Oldie gets up with a little help from me.

"Will they be cross with me?"

I look over at our group. Mohamed has just advised them that Old Oldie has been found and is OK. He sees us and waves heartily. Then our whole group turns and waves and a cheer goes up.

"No, they won't be cross."

I take Old Oldie's arm and we walk slowly back to the proper restaurant. She says, "I'm very tired, you know. Perhaps I wasn't thinking straight."

"It doesn't matter. We're all just relieved that you are alright. And none of us will blame you for feeling tired. It's been a busy few days. And you worked hard to keep up."

"I certainly did. But, oh my, I am so glad I came! I would not have missed this for the world."

I couldn't agree more.

Old Oldie is greeted like a conquering hero and there is laughter and toasting in her honour. And once again I am feel that sense of family that such a group develops on a tour like this. It is pretty special.

Hubby has been delegated to speak a few words on behalf of our group before the dinner finishes. He thanks Mohamed and we all cheer. He thanks everyone on the tour for being such a great bunch of people, carefully avoiding the gaze of Ms Miseryguts and Mrs Love-a-Chat. Then we charge our glasses and raise them to Egypt. It is a wonderful note to finish on.

We board the bus and go back to the hotel. In the foyer, we all say a few words, wave to each other and go to our rooms. For me and Hubby, it is a welcome nap after so big a lunch. After the nap, we pack our bags and all the tour pamphlets, then get out the information for the next tour we are joining in Italy in a few days. We have booked a hotel in the Prati District in Rome for four days before joining our next tour. We've been to Italy before, it is my favourite destination, and we plan to wander around Rome at leisure before the pace heats up again.

And we don't go down to the dining room for dinner. We have said our farewells and are already mentally moving on. Sharing space with our group now would be a bit of an anti-climax. So we order room service, just a little soup and salad, and sit for one last time on our room balcony with our own private view of the Nile and busy, amazing Cairo sliding into the evening. I remark to Hubby that my gut feels fine, so I have avoided Cairo Tummy. I feel a little smug. After all, I was so very careful, except for that one slip this morning. It's all good. Life is good.

DAY 11

DEPARTURE

I spoke too soon.

I wake up the next morning feeling a tad nauseated. It's not too bad, maybe it will come to nothing. Nevertheless, Hubby fishes out the packet of antibiotics we bought over the counter when we first arrived in Egypt. I take a double dose and hope for the best.

Our flight leaves mid morning. We go to reception and check our baggage in for the shuttle bus to the airport. Then we go to the dining room for breakfast.

I don't see anyone we know there. Some early flights and would have left by now. Others left yesterday. We sit down and I order black tea. My stomach isn't up to anything else. But I'm still not feeling too bad.

Hubby tucks into a full English breakfast and I have to look away.

I hear a familiar voice behind me. "What time are you flying out?"

I turn to find the owner of that voice. It had sounded so familiar. That squeaky, slightly apologetic tone. I thought it was Mrs Teetering Heels, but she is nowhere to be seen.

I turn back to see Hubby holding a sausage on a fork before him and staring open mouthed over my shoulder. He blinks at me. I turn around and look again.

It takes a second. But there she is. Limp, freshly washed hair with that long bit at the front clipped behind her ear, no makeup, wrinkles laid bare, bags under the eyes, a substantial turkey neck, and dressed in a voluminous beige t-shirt, a calf-length denim skirt that actually fits and - wonder upon wonder - black orthopaedic slip-on flats. Rather worn, comfortable flats. So she does wear flat shoes after all. I am seeing the real woman for the first time, the woman at home doing the washing and cooking the dinner. And she's rather lovely.

I am trying my best not to show my surprise and say quickly, "Our flight leaves at 11.30. What about yours?"

Mr Teetering Heels has been watching my face. He smirks a little and I get the impression he's seen this reaction before. "This afternoon. 2.45pm. Where are you off to next?"

"Italy for two and a half weeks, then a garden tour of Europe for a month."

Mrs Teetering Heels says, "That's a long time to be away from home."

"It's winter in Canberra. It'll be down to minus 10 degrees there soon. We like to escape the worst of it if we can. Where are you off to next?"

"Home," she says with some relief. "I need my physio. Everything feels thrown out. My back and my neck and my hips. You know what I mean?"

I nod as if I do, but I won't need physio when I get home because I have worn sensible shoes for the whole trip. I open my mouth to say as much, change my mind and say instead, "Indeed I do. Well, have a good trip home. It's been lovely sharing Egypt with you."

She grins broadly. "And with you. Safe travels."

We turn back to our breakfast. Hubby and I bend out heads over our cups of tea and try not to look at each other. We are both looking a little stunned, and we wouldn't offend that dear lady for anything in the world.

I hope her physio sorted her out.

It's in the shuttle bus that I feel the nausea increase. I begin feeling a bit clammy and shaky, but the wheels have been set in motion and there is no going back. We check in at the airport and find a cafe to while away the next couple of hours. And then it hits the bowel. I rush to the nearest toilet and only just make it in time. Oh gawd, is there anything more embarrassing than diarrhoea in a public toilet, accompanied as it is with much farting and exploding? Not to mention the cleaning up afterward.

Never travel without a good supply of tissues and wet wipes in your bag!

If you find yourself in such a situation, just remember to stay in the cubicle long enough for the people who have heard and smelled your agony to leave and a fresh lot of women to fill the surrounding cubicles. That way, when you do leave, no one will know who is responsible for the aroma. And look incredibly innocent and unaware as you wash your hands and walk out. It wasn't me, Mum!

I join Hubby, only to dash to the toilets again a few moments later.

I return to Hubby feeling decidedly weak and shaky. We are both feeling really concerned now. We have to board a plane shortly. Am I going to get on it without mishap? We hear our flight called and I feel the urge again. And it's desperate. I rush to the loo and repeat the first two experiences. When I come out, Hubby hands me another antibiotic. It's all I can do to keep it down.

And then I remember the tale one of our young relatives told us. He had been travelling in Thailand and had just boarded the plane home to Australia when the bug hit him as the plane taxied along the runway. He was wearing baggy cargo shorts, as you do when travelling in Asia, and tried to get up to go to the toilet, but the flight attendants ordered him to stay seated and strapped in until the seatbelt sign went off. As the plane left the ground, so the contents of his bowel left him. Right there in his seat. There wasn't a thing he could do to stop it. He said the smell filled the plane and everyone was gagging and complaining, but he was sitting in a pile of poo and couldn't move. It couldn't get any worse than that. The plane reached it's desired altitude, the seatbelt sign went off and the flight attendants converged on him. They helped him up and led him to the toilet, whereupon the faeces departed the containment of his cargo shorts and ran down his legs onto the floor, leaving a trail of poop behind him. It had just got worse. The flight attendants did their best to clean him up, but he had nothing to change into, so they found a towel and he spent the rest of the flight sitting with a towel wrapped around his waist in another seat up front where no one could look at him face to face. The flight crew spent a lot of time with sponges and bottles of disinfectant until all visible signs of the accident were gone, but without fresh air inside that plane, it stank of faeces and disinfectant all the way back to Australia. A memorable journey for everyone, for all the wrong reasons.

Was that to be my fate now?

We line up to board. As I show my boarding pass to the flight attendant, I say quietly, "I've got an upset stomach. I'll need the toilet as soon as I get on the plane."

She nods knowingly. Clearly, I am not the first person she's seen with this problem. "Just tell them as you get on. They'll take care of you."

As we step onto the plane, I inform the pretty young woman directing passengers to their seats. She also nods knowingly and whispers, "There are a few empty seats at the front next to the toilets. Sit there." She points them out and we take our seats. No sooner have I sat down than I am up again and hitting that plane loo with everything I have. I can hear other passengers boarding on the other side of the loo door and hope that the smell is not making its way past the door.

When I take my seat again, I am feeling weak and washed out. Hubby hands me a bottle of water.

"Sip," he says encouragingly and, not for the first time, I am so grateful not to be travelling alone.

I make it through the ascent, the seatbelt sign goes off and I'm up and away again. Two more episodes and we arrive at the Rome airport. It's an airport loo as soon as we disembark and then we are lining up at Customs with what seems like thousands of others. It's a long, long line. My belly ain't behaving and I need a loo desperately. I look around, but cannot see one anywhere. I am sweating and shaking and Hubby says I look awful. And I can feel an encore of the Customs episode in Australia coming on.

I approach one of the uniformed Italian officers standing nearby. I say, "Is there a toilet nearby?"

He looks me up and down and his eyes narrow. "You need a toilet, madam?" he says in heavily accented English.

"Yes, I have a tummy bug." I rub my tummy and grimace.

"You will have to wait until you get through Customs."

Oh gawd, am I going to make it?

He waves to another officer, whispers something in his ear, and lo and behold, we are taken to the front of the queue. I am so grateful.

But wait, all is not as it seems. Several uniformed officers descend on us and we must stand with

270

our arms held out while they run their drug testing devices over us. Then an officer with a drug sniffer dog arrives and we and our luggage get the full treatment. I realise they suspect I am carrying drugs internally and that perhaps one of the balloons has broken inside me. I watch those border patrol and airport programs on TV. I know how this goes down. Oh gawd, are they going to do an internal search? I sweat and shake even more.

Hubby is in full discussion with two guards, explaining the Cairo Tummy, my foolishness in washing my hair under the shower, how it hit me at the Cairo airport. Then he produces the antibiotics and shows them how many tablets I've taken. And it seems to work. They back off. Their devices and the dog have indicated we are clean and they let us through. Just in time. I find the nearest loo and away we go again.

We find a taxi and get to our hotel. We had planned to have dinner at one of the fabulous local restaurants. I am crazy about Italian food, especially in Italy. But all I can manage when I get to our room is to fall on the bed and lie there like a limp rag. And so my first day in beautiful Italy is spent going back and forth to the toilet while Hubby goes out to forage for food and supplies. He comes back with some very upmarket Italian take-away and a bit of a sore throat and cough.

He has caught the mandatory tour bug that three of our comrades had bought onto the bus back in Egypt. The incubation period for that bug is ten to fourteen days, so I guess that makes sense.

I am exhausted by nightfall and the antibiotics are finally kicking in. I sleep like a log and when I wake the next morning, I am feeling much better, although Hubby is rather seedy. But he is not one to let a touch of the flu stop him. We can begin our Italy trip.

In a few days, we will be joining another tour with another set of eccentric, endlessly interesting Old Farts for two and a half weeks. And yet another set of Old Farts on our month long garden tour after that.

All part of the package tour experience. I am looking forward to it.

But that is another story for another day.

THE END

A PLACE IN TIME
By C. A. HOCKING

Dan Campbell is a troubled man who sinks into depression as each birthday approaches. Thirty years earlier, on his 11th birthday, he'd witnessed his father's murder and saved his mother from a deranged stranger, but something is wrong with the memory of that terrible day. Something he can't quite see, something just out of focus.

When his annual depression threatens his family's wellbeing, he goes back to his childhood home to confront his memories and find answers to the mystery of his father's death.

Dan is swept back in time to the day of the murder and what he discovers there will turn his world upside down, for no one and nothing is as he remembers. And the truth is more shocking than he could ever have imagined.

DAMAGED GOODS
By C. A. HOCKING

Damaged Goods is a gripping gothic saga about three young sisters trapped in a childhood of unrelenting abuse at the hands of their cruel father. In order to survive their nightmare, Helen, Sis and Sweetypie create a secret world for themselves where their love for each other sustains them.

But children grow up and the day comes when the sisters know they must end their torment, whatever it takes. They plot a brutal revenge on their father, but not all goes as planned and Helen finds herself fleeing her family home and her beloved sisters.

Fifty years after leaving, Helen returns to find Sis and Sweetypie much as she had left them. Or so it seems at first, until she discovers secrets within secrets and an act of vengeance that still haunts their lives. So begins a journey for each of them that will ultimately end in tragedy, closure and release.

HOME TO ROOST
By C. A. HOCKING

Australian Prime Minister Marian Hardwick has achieved everything she ever desired to become the most powerful woman in the country. She is admired by some, but seen as ruthless, calculating and manipulative by others.

Only two men really know her — her husband and her brother — but one loves her and the other hates her. When one threatens to destroy her by revealing a secret buried deep in her past, the other can save her, but first he must break her completely.

Marian's life unravels as everything she ever believed in is exposed as a lie. If she is to survive, she must confront the greatest challenge of all — the truth about herself.

SARAH ANN ELLIOTT
Book 1: 1823-1829
An Epic Family Saga based on a true story.
By C. A. HOCKING

Sarah Ann Elliott was born in 1823 into a family of weavers whose lives were entirely dependent on the textile mills of the booming Northern England town of Stockport.

Her family is much like any other with highs and lows, joys and sorrows, but when 10,000 spinners and weavers go on strike for nine months in the infamous 1829 Stockport Turnout, the Elliotts are plunged into a life of hardship and turmoil from which no one is spared.

Little Sarah Ann is swept along with the events that surround her and it is only the love of her family and her indomitable spirit that will carry her through.

AUNT EDNA and The Lightning Rock
Book 1 of The AUNT EDNA STORIES
by C. A. HOCKING

When Aunt Edna learns that her 11 year-old orphaned niece, Isobel is coming to live with her, she has a panic attack. Goodness, whatever will she do with a niece? After all, Aunt Edna is an Eternal with magical powers and Isobel is a Mere Mortal.

And what will Diggidydog, Grumblebumkin, The Great Smoking Beastie and Barking Wood Stove make of a niece? Not to mention the five Ghosts on the veranda and Frozen Bert in the freezer.

An Australian Children's Fable
of Weirdness and Wonder!

Made in the USA
Monee, IL
12 August 2023

40914103R00163